# SPOTLIGHT ON SUFFIXES

## Book One

# Common Suffixes
# and
# Suffixing Rules

# Book One
# Common Suffixes
# and
# Suffixing Rules

First edition published by
The Robinswood Press  2000

Design and illustrations:
© Stephen Emms, Phil Goundrey, Sue Kruse and The Robinswood Press 2000.
This version (v1.2) printed by Blueprint Design & Graphics Ltd.

## The Robinswood Press

Stourbridge   England

ISBN 1-869981-60X

# CONTENTS

## Appendices

# ABOUT THE AUTHOR

## Gillian Aitken MA, PGCE, RSA Dip. TEFL, AMBDA, Dip. Psych. (Open)

Gillian Aitken trained originally as an English teacher and taught in schools for a number of years. More recently she has concentrated on areas in teaching English where a specialised approach is required. These have included teaching English to pupils with Special Needs, teaching pupils where English is a Second or a Foreign Language, and adult literacy work with the Dyslexia Institute.

Ms Aitken therefore has a unique range of experience gained practically both in Britain and abroad, and through further academic study. This background has provided her with both a clear understanding of the challenges faced by teachers in a variety of different situations and also perfect opportunities to develop a variety of exercises – such as the word-search exercises in her first publication, *Spotlight on Words,* the consonant blend exercises of *Spotlight on Blends* Books One and Two, and now the Suffix exercises in *Spotlight on Suffixes* Books One and Two. All these exercises meet the educationalist's requirement to build spelling and reading skills whilst the pupil becomes engrossed in the challenge and enjoyment of the exercises themselves.

Ms Aitken lives in Sussex and continues to work as a specialist English teacher. She is an Associate Member of the British Dyslexia Association and a Graduate Member of the British Psychological Society.

# INTRODUCTION

Suffixes are a very important part of the English language system. If one were to read any page of print at random, it is likely that between 15% and 25% of the words would have a suffix. *Spotlight on Suffixes,* Book One, aims to raise awareness about this very important area of language, teaching not only the grammatical function of suffixes, but the rules by which suffixes are added to base words. Pupils will thus improve their knowledge of grammar, vocabulary and spelling by doing the various worksheets. It is hoped that a systematic approach to suffixing will reduce many common spelling errors in later life which reflect lack of awareness about word structure, as well as confusion about which rule to follow when adding suffixes to base words. The suffixes dealt with in Book One are the most common ones in English, deriving from Anglo-Saxon, and thus the essential building blocks of the English language.

The book introduces each suffix separately, starting with the most common suffixes 's', 'es', 'ing' and 'ed'. There are at least two worksheets on each suffix, the first one teaching the grammatical function and use of the suffix, and the second (or subsequent ones) giving practice of the relevant suffixing rules. Some suffixes, however, are dealt with in more depth. The suffix 'ed' is complicated by the fact that it can be pronounced in three different ways depending on the base word, and therefore sound discrimination exercises have been included, as well as a focus on adding 'ed' to base words ending in double consonants and consonant blends.

The suffixing rules are introduced gradually, with on-going recycling of the *double* and *drop 'e'* rules as each new vowel suffix is introduced. The *change 'y' to 'i'* rule is first introduced in the context of making words plural (Worksheets 12 and 13), and the general rule is then made explicit when the consonant suffixes 'ful', 'less' and 'ness' are introduced. It is recommended that pupils are fully conversant with the *double* and *drop 'e'* rules before being introduced to the *change* rule, or confusion will arise.

The worksheets vary in format, although many sentence completion exercises have been included in order to provide context for the suffixes being introduced. For these exercises it is suggested that pupils work out the answers by themselves, or orally with the teacher, and then complete the sentences without referring to the words printed on the page. It will thus be necessary to mask the top part of the page. In this way, pupils will have to think more carefully about how to spell the target words, using the correct rule. Other exercises involve Word-squares, anagrams, word tracking, text reading for suffix recognition, and sentence writing. Answers to the Word-squares are given at the back of the book.

The last section of the book (Worksheets 57-75) consists of suffix revision exercises, with specific revision exercises on the three main suffixing rules. The rule practice sheets enable the various rules to be practised with all the suffixes which have been taught in the book. There are answers to Worksheets 71-75 at the back of the book.

It is hoped that the clear and uncluttered layout will make the worksheets easy to use for both pupil and teacher. This is particularly important for Special Needs pupils. For consistency and clarity, each suffix is enclosed inside a box, which pupils can colour or highlight if they wish. Many of the worksheets contain a spelling rule which is printed clearly inside a box at the top of the page. Important grammatical terms such as 'noun', 'adjective', etc., are printed in capitals and underlined for emphasis.

Detailed teaching notes and guidelines on the various suffixes are given, with suggestions about using the worksheets and highlighting possible areas of confusion or difficulty. At the back of the book there are also separate appendices consisting of word lists for the various suffixes. These can be a useful source of reference for teachers wishing to make their own worksheets or to provide further practice exercises on specific suffixes or rules. Appendix 10 describes how the final rule practice sheets (Worksheets 73-75) can be adapted to a suffixing card game.

Teachers will have to use their own judgement in order to decide when to use the various worksheets. Specific knowledge about suffixing should be an integral part of any structured literacy programme, and indeed the Government's National Literacy Strategy places distinct emphasis on this area of language throughout the Junior School years. It is hoped that the material in this book will be a useful resource to busy teachers trying to implement this programme, or indeed to any teacher involved in literacy teaching. Although a few of the worksheets are clearly suited to very young children because of the pictorial content, the material is generally adaptable to a wide age range.

**Gillian Aitken**

# TEACHING NOTES AND GUIDELINES

## Worksheets 1-5       s

This suffix as a noun plural ending can be introduced in the very earliest stage of reading and writing, and **Worksheets 1 and 2** use only one-syllable words with short vowels, or common, high frequency words such as 'book' or 'ball'. The concept of 's' as a plural noun ending is a very concrete one, making this an ideal way to introduce the idea of suffixes to young children as an ending which can be taken on or off words according to the meaning. Getting children to write simple plural words on cards and then physically cut off the 's' ending is a good way to teach the concept before using worksheets as consolidation.

Suffix 's' as a verb ending is a much more difficult concept, as children often find it hard to identify verbs, and the 's' ending is only used in the third person. **Worksheet 3** will thus need careful teacher input. The model sentences can be written on the board before the worksheet is given out, and teachers can explore what kind of words 'plays', 'meets', etc., are, and then use simple verbs with a variety of subjects such as 'I', 'The children', 'John', etc., so that pupils can work out the rule for themselves. It is not necessary to use grammatical phrases like 'third person singular', but pupils should work out that the 's' ending is only used when the subject is 'He', 'She' or 'It' or when the noun itself is used instead of the pronoun. Of course, pupils are not likely to omit the 's' ending in their own language usage unless English is not their first language, but exploring the 's' ending will raise their language awareness. The gap-filling exercise in **Worksheet 3** is fairly straightforward, but pupils will have to pay careful attention to the subject in order to choose the correct verb ending. The exercise on 'Keep Fit Frank' will extend more able pupils who can use their imagination, and reinforce the idea that the Simple Present tense, which requires the 's' suffix ending, is often used to describe habitual, regular actions or activities.

**Worksheet 4** contrasts the noun and verb function of suffix 's', and is a good way of checking that pupils have understood the basic difference between verbs and nouns. The writing exercise will encourage pupils to use their imagination, and children should enjoy the novelty of writing about such a strange person.

**Worksheet 5**, which involves sound discrimination, highlights the fact that the letter 's' has two very different sounds. For pupils who have difficulty in sound processing, or who tend to spell words just as they sound, this type of sound discrimination and awareness is necessary. The letter 'z', in fact, is rarely used for the /z/ sound, whereas the letter 's' often has this voiced sound. All children should be made aware of this, as young children tend to think there is a one-to-one correspondence between letters and sounds which is very far from the truth in English.

## Worksheets 6-14       es

Suffix 'es' fulfils the same grammatical function as suffix 's', so the concept should not be a problem if pupils are familiar with suffix 's' as a noun and verb ending. However, there are spelling rules governing the use of suffix 'es' which need to be taught carefully and systematically to avoid confusion between the two suffixes, or the common error of using apostrophe 's instead of 'es' suffix which teachers are all too familiar with! The basic rule is that suffix 'es' is used instead of 's' on base words ending with 's' or 'ss', 'sh', 'x' and 'ch', and **Worksheets 6-9** give practice of these word endings. Ideally, these worksheets should be used when children are working generally on words ending in 'ss', 'sh', etc., if they are following a structured literacy programme. Once the basic rules have been covered, **Worksheets 10 and 11** can be used to draw together the endings which require the 'es' suffix. **Worksheet 11** is more challenging than number **10** as it contrasts suffix 's' with suffix 'es', requiring pupils to look carefully at the structure of base words. Some children internalise the wrong rule about use of suffix 'es', and put it on words which end in consonant blends such as 'sk' or 'sp'. Exercise B in **Worksheet 11** will show whether a child is still confused about when to use this suffix so that the correct rule can be revised and further practice given if necessary.

The other main use of suffix 'es' is on base words ending in 'y' preceded by a consonant when the 'y' changes to 'i'. Very often this is taught just in the context of noun plural endings, but the same rule is applied when 'es' is a verb ending. **Worksheet 13** gives practice of both nouns and verbs ending in 'y' which require *changing 'y' to 'i'* before adding suffix 'es'. The above spelling rule is a fairly complex one requiring a great deal of practice and consolidation for it to be applied automatically. **Worksheet 12** states the rule very simply, but before giving pupils the worksheet, the teacher could present a selection of nouns ending in 'y' and ask them how they think the plural is spelt. This will probably lead to some incorrect guesses, but by putting the correct plural forms on the board, the pupils can be challenged to work the rule out for themselves. Very often a clue is needed, which is to ask pupils to look at the letter before 'y' in the base words. Words ending in 'y' can often be tricky to spell, and as this rule is complex, it should not be introduced until a pupil has progressed well beyond the initial stages of a structured literacy programme. In the National Literacy Strategy, it is taught in Term 1 of Year 5. There is further consolidation of the *change 'y' to 'i'* rule in the Suffix Revision section (**Worksheet 67**), and teachers can make their own practice sheets by looking at the list of words ending in 'y' in Appendix 3.

Finally, **Worksheet 14** focuses on suffix 'es' added to words ending in 'o' which are mainly nouns apart from the very common, but frequently mis-spelt words 'does' and 'goes'. Pupils should not be taught that all words ending in 'o' take the 'es' suffix. In fact, the majority of such words are of foreign origin and take the normal suffix 's' such as 'pianos', 'studios', etc. There are also a few words ending in 'o' where the choice of suffix is optional in the plural such as 'mosquito'. The words in **Worksheet 14**, however, are the most common ones taking 'es' suffix. Most of these words should be familiar to most children of eight years or above, although it is possible that some children will not know what a 'tornado' or even a 'buffalo' is. In this case, they might need some help in unscrambling the words. Some children find anagrams very difficult, in which case they should be given the first letter or two to avoid frustration.

# Worksheets 15-21       ing

The suffix 'ing' is so common that children will encounter it as soon as they begin to read their first reading books. Grammatically, this suffix is complex in that it has many functions. It can be a noun (e.g. 'Shopping is fun'), an adjective (e.g. boring book) and a verb participle ending, denoting either the present or past continuous tense. However, it is best understood as a verb ending, and **Worksheets 15 and 16** introduce this suffix in a very concrete fashion in the context of present action. These worksheets are aimed at Year 1 and Year 2 pupils to enable them to recognise this suffix as an ending on words which tell us what people are doing now. Simple, everyday verbs are used, and pupils should be encouraged to suggest some other common verbs. Such work on suffixes and grammar should, of course, be linked to other literacy work, and children should be asked to look for 'ing' words in their reading books.

**Worksheets 17 to 21** focus on the spelling rules by which 'ing' is added to base words. Pupils in Year 3 are expected to become familiar with these rules, although teachers will have to use their own judgement in deciding when their pupils are old enough to understand and apply the rules, and are advised to teach each rule separately with a suitable time interval before introducing the next rule in order to avoid confusion. The *doubling* rule is a very important one for English spelling, and explains why so many words such as 'rabbit' and 'holly' are spelt with double letters in the middle. Teachers should stress the necessity of *doubling* to protect the short vowel, and invite pupils to suggest how words would be pronounced if the *doubling* rule was not applied, e.g. 'waging' instead of 'wagging'. As other vowel suffixes are introduced in the book, there is constant re-cycling of both the *doubling* and *drop 'e'* rules which need a great deal of practice and consolidation to be applied automatically. **Worksheet 21** is an example of a rule practice sheet contrasting the *double* and *drop 'e'* suffixing rules, and teachers can very quickly and easily make up similar practice sheets by using the word lists in Appendix 1 and 2.

# Worksheets 22-32       ed

This suffix is treated in more detail than other suffixes, not only because it is so common, but because it can be pronounced in three different ways depending on the structure of the base word. This can lead to spelling errors with young children or older dyslexic pupils who tend to spell words as they sound.

**Worksheets 22 and 23** introduce the concept of 'ed' as a past tense verb ending, although by doing **Worksheet 22** pupils will no doubt use some irregular past tense verbs when asked to write down five things they did yesterday and last week. This can lead to awareness of regular verbs requiring the 'ed' suffix in the past tense, and the many common verbs such as 'eat', 'drink' and 'see', etc., which form the past tense in a different way.

**Worksheet 23** uses the 'ed' suffix in the context of a story, and encourages pupils to finish the story for themselves. The wonderful poem 'The Listeners' by Walter de la Mare would be a very suitable literary text to do in conjunction with this Worksheet, perhaps focusing on the theme of mystery and suspense.

**Worksheets 24 and 25** give practice in sound discrimination.

Dyslexic pupils whose core difficulty is phonological processing have great difficulty with this suffix. Without careful training, they will spell this ending as it sounds (e.g., 'stuft' for 'stuffed'), or very often they will omit the suffix altogether. For this reason, **Worksheets 26-28** give specific practice in some of the endings which cause problems when suffix 'ed' is added. These endings tend to be the double letter endings (base words ending in 'ss', 'll', 'ck' and 'ff'), and base words endings in consonant blends such as 'mp' and 'nt'. Pupils should be encouraged to count syllables when adding 'ed' to base words, recognising that with some base words (e.g., words ending in 'nd' or 'nt') the 'ed' suffix adds an extra syllable to the word. But when suffix 'ed' has a /d/ or /t/ sound, no extra syllable is added.

**Worksheets 29-32** give further practice of the *double* and *drop 'e'* rules, and adding 'ed' to words ending in 'y' preceded by a vowel. **Worksheet 29** is designed to train pupils to spot the doubling pattern visually, and many pupils internalise this rule very quickly. For those pupils who do not find it easy to spot the pattern, they should be encouraged to mark the word pattern of the base word. Pupils are not likely to mis-spell words such as 'waved' when the base word ends in 'e', but **Worksheet 30** makes them aware that they are actually following the *drop 'e'* rule in such words, a fact they might not have been aware of. Adding 'ed' to words ending in 'y' is a common cause of spelling error (e.g., 'stayed' spelt as 'stade'), and **Worksheet 31** aims to clarify this by focusing on words ending in 'ay', 'ey' or 'oy' which *just add* the suffix. At this stage pupils are not introduced to base words such as 'apply' which end in 'y' preceded by a consonant, as this would necessitate teaching the *change 'y' to 'i'* rule. (This is first introduced in the context of adding consonant suffixes 'ful', 'less' and 'ness' to base words in **Worksheet 41**, while **Worksheet 67** in the Rule Revision section gives specific practice of adding 'ed' to various words ending in 'y'.)

# Worksheets 33-35          y

This is an extremely common suffix as can be judged by the length of the word list in Appendix 4, and derives from the Anglo Saxon suffix 'ig'. Unlike the other suffixes introduced so far, suffix 'y' is an adjective suffix, and work on this suffix should be a useful complement to grammar work on the recognition and function of adjectives. Pupils should understand how the addition of 'y' changes a noun (e.g., rain) into an adjective which can then be used to define further nouns (e.g., rainy day). **Worksheet 33** requires pupils to think of nouns which can go with adjectives ending in 'y'. As many weather words end in 'y', it was thought useful to focus on these words in this introductory worksheet. **Worksheet 34** recycles the *double* and *drop 'e'* rules which are necessary in many cases as 'y' is a vowel suffix. Many pupils fail to apply the *drop 'e'* rule to words ending in 'y', producing errors such as 'wobbley' and 'shiney', so particular practice is needed with these words. (Appendix 4 includes a selection of base words ending in 'e' to which suffix 'y' can be added.) **Worksheet 35** is a vocabulary quiz requiring pupils to unscramble base words describing personal characteristics and then adding suffix 'y' by following the correct rule. As for other exercises with anagrams, pupils who find this sort of exercise difficult should be given the first letter.

## Worksheets 36-42      ful     less     ness

These suffixes are introduced in succession as they all begin with consonants and therefore, in most cases, are just added to base words. The suffix rules are dealt with in **Worksheet 41** which also gives some introductory practice of *changing 'y' to 'i'* in words like 'merciful' and 'happiness'.

Suffix 'ful' is introduced in a very concrete way in **Worksheet 36**, making this worksheet suitable for pupils in Year 2. Later on, pupils can learn the most common function of 'ful' as an ending which changes nouns into adjectives meaning 'full of' (**Worksheet 37**). It should be stressed to pupils that when 'ful' is used as a suffix, it only has one 'l'. The suffix 'less' is, of course, the inverse of 'ful', although many base words can only be used with either 'ful' or 'less'. Base words like 'care' which can take either suffix are not that common. In **Worksheet 39** pupils are asked to add 'less' to a number of base words, and then find the six base words which can also take suffix 'ful'. Other base words which can take both suffixes are: 'cheer', 'doubt', 'faith', 'help', 'joy', 'law', 'mercy', 'pity', 'shame', 'tact', 'thank', and 'tune'.

The suffix 'ness' (**Worksheet 40**) introduces a new concept, namely that of abstract nouns, and could be used as part of a grammar lesson on this topic. Pupils are reminded that when adding 'ness' to a base word ending in 'n' such as 'mean', the new word will have a double 'n' in the middle. **Worksheet 42** brings together 'ful', 'less' and 'ness', and the first exercise consists of a sentence completion task in which pupils have to choose the correct suffix. The second exercise is a focus on adding two suffixes to base words, thus training children to become more aware of word structure.

## Worksheets 43-45      ly

The suffix 'ly' is the adverb suffix in English, although a few words ending in 'ly' are actually adjectives (e.g., 'lovely', 'friendly' and 'lively'). The main function of adverbs is to modify verbs, and this is the main teaching point of **Worksheet 43**. However, adverbs can also modify adjectives or other adverbs (e.g., 'extremely clever' or 'incredibly quickly'), or can modify a whole sentence (e.g., 'Actually, I don't believe you.'). The use of 'ly' as adjective modifier is dealt with in *Spotlight on Suffixes,* Book 2. **Worksheet 43** introduces a selection of adverbs with missing vowels, and pupils are required to complete the word from their own knowledge, or to use dictionaries or spellcheckers for the more difficult words. They then have to choose four adverbs from the list to modify seven common verbs. Pupils should be encouraged to use four different adverbs for each verb, which might necessitate changing their choice as they work through each verb. They can, of course, use different adverbs if they wish, but it is not always easy to think of appropriate adverbs, which is why the adverb list was given to pupils rather than asking them to come up with their own list.

**Worksheet 44** focuses on the spelling rules by which 'ly' is added to base words, which gives further practice of the 'y' to 'i' rule (e.g., happily). It should also be pointed out that, if the base word ends in the suffix 'ful', the complete word will have a double 'll' (e.g., hopefully). It is a common error to spell such words with only one 'l'. **Worksheet 45** gives practice in adding two suffixes to base words, and pupils must be taught to apply their suffixing rules sequentially when adding both suffixes (e.g., 'amaze'+'ing'+'ly' requires the *drop 'e'* rule and *just add* rule). There are further practice exercises in adding two suffixes to base words in the suffixing revision section (**Worksheets 57 and 58**).

# Worksheets 46 and 47  en

This suffix has two main functions. The most common one is a verb ending, changing an adjective into a verb meaning 'to make' or 'to become', and this is the focus of **Worksheets 46 and 47**. However, it is also a verb participle ending on irregular verbs such as 'driven' and as such is found in passive constructions. This use, which is less common, is not included in order to avoid confusion, but is covered in Book 2. **Worksheet 46** aims at recognition and is very straightforward, although the second exercise encourages pupils to think about word meanings. **Worksheet 47** is slightly more challenging, but most pupils enjoy doing Word-squares, and the task is made easier by the fact that the first letter and length of each word are given.

# Worksheets 48 and 49  ish

The main uses of suffix 'ish' are given at the top of **Worksheet 48**, and pupils are reminded that 'ish' is a vowel suffix, so that they might have to apply the *double* or *drop 'e'* rule when adding it to base words. If pupils are having trouble with the anagrams in the second exercise, point out that each word ends in 'ish', so that once these letters are crossed off, there are not many left to unscramble. **Worksheet 49** requires pupils to track base words in a line of letters to which suffix 'ish' can be added, and then use the word to complete the accompanying sentence. Not all pupils might be familiar with the word 'sheepish' (No. 2) or 'boorish' (No. 10), so might need help. For No. 8, some pupils might come up with 'wimpish' as the missing word, but this does not make sense. The answer is, of course, 'impish'. If teachers wish to introduce more words with suffix 'ish', they can refer to the word list in Appendix 7. This suffix is not as common as the other suffixes introduced so far, although many people add 'ish' to all kinds of words to convey the idea of 'a little bit'. It might be interesting to discuss with pupils this idea of using language creatively and individually. Teachers can ask their class for suggestions, and then decide together which words would be acceptable if they were compiling a dictionary, and which would be excluded because they sound 'over-the-top'.

# Worksheets 50-56       er      est

The suffix 'er' is first introduced as an adjective ending meaning 'more', and should thus be linked to grammar work on the formation of comparatives and superlatives in English. **Worksheet 50** gives further practice of the *double* and *drop 'e'* suffixing rules, but does not include adjectives ending in 'y' which would necessitate *changing 'y' to 'i'*. **Worksheets 51 and 52** focus on suffix 'er' as agent. In **Worksheet 51** pupils have to give their own examples of both things and people which end in 'er'. For the second exercise, tell pupils not to choose words from the exercise below for examples of people who do jobs or activities! It should be easy to come up with other examples as this is a very common ending. The third exercise on adding 'er' to base words gives further practice of the *double* and *drop 'e'* rules, but not the *change 'y' to 'i'* rule. **Worksheet 52** is a Word-square in which pupils must find words ending in 'er' to match the meanings given below. This time they are given the number of letters, but not the first letter. However, most of the words are fairly common, although 'trader' going downwards has proved a stumbling block.

**Worksheet 53** teaches the 'y' to 'i' rule in words ending in 'y', and then gives practice of all the suffixing rules in the second exercise. If pupils have already come across the *change* rule before, this can be a useful revision exercise. **Worksheet 54** brings together the two functions of 'er' suffix, asking pupils to categorise a list of words ending in 'er' according to the function of the suffix. There is also a focus on suffixing rules, although this time pupils have to look at the word to which 'er' has already been added, and work out what rule was used. This kind of exercise is a good way of assessing whether a pupil understands how suffixing rules work, and teaches them to think logically and analytically.

**Worksheet 55** introduces suffix 'est' to mean 'most', and should obviously be linked to suffix 'er' meaning 'more'. **Worksheet 56** contrasts both 'er' and 'est' in a straightforward sentence completion exercise. It can be pointed out that we always use the word 'the' before words with 'est' suffix. The second exercise in this worksheet recycles 'est' in the form of a general knowledge quiz. For teachers whose general knowledge might not be as good as their pupils, the answers are given below!

1   Ben Nevis (1343 metres high).

2   Loch Ness (mean depth 130 metres).

3   Oxford (first college founded in 1249).

4   The Queen.

5   The blue whale (over 30 metres long and weighs over 150 tonnes!).

6   The Nile.

7   Pluto.

8   Asia.

# Worksheets 57-75      Suffix Revision and Rule Practice Sheets

The last section of the book consists of suffix revision and rule practice sheets. No new suffixes are introduced. The first five revision sheets (**Worksheets 57-61**) involve tasks such as identifying missing suffixes on words; choosing the correct suffix to complete words; identifying the base word in words with one or more suffixes; and adding one or more suffixes to base words. **Worksheets 59-61** are identical in format, but there is a gradual gradation in difficulty in that **Worksheet 59** uses words with only one suffix, **Worksheet 60** uses words with two suffixes, while **Worksheet 61** uses all the suffixing rules for the second exercise, including the change rule.

The following six worksheets (**Worksheets 62-67**) revise each of the three main rules: *doubling, drop 'e'* and *change 'y' to 'i'*. There are two revision sheets on each rule. For the *doubling* and *drop 'e'* rule, the first sheet requires pupils to identify the word sums which require application of the rule, while the second sheet contrasts the rule with words which *just add* the suffix to the base word. The first revision sheet on the *change* rule, **Worksheet 66**, requires pupils to discriminate between a variety of base words ending in 'y'. They have to identify which *just add* the suffix, and which require application of the *change 'y' to 'i'* rule. **Worksheet 67** consists of two exercises, the first requiring pupils to add suffix 'ed' to 20 words ending in 'y', while in the second exercise they have to give the plural form of a further 20 words ending in 'y' by *just adding* suffix 's' or *changing 'y' to 'i'* and adding suffix 'es'.

**Worksheets 68-70** are identical in format and level of difficulty. They involve all the suffixing rules, but instead of adding the suffix to base words, pupils instead have to identify the base word and state the rule by which the suffix was added to the base word. **Worksheets 71 and 72** are straightforward rule practice sheets, but only involve the *double, drop 'e'* and *just add* rules. The last three worksheets involve all the suffixing rules, and pupils can be asked to monitor their performance by keeping a record of both their score and time when doing such sheets. A blank master sheet with the same format is included so that teachers can make up their own practice sheets as necessary, using the word lists at the back of the book. There is also a suggestion in Appendix 10 for recycling the same rules in the form of a game.

# Suffix 2 NOUN or NOUNS?

**Why do we put s at the end of words?**

I have an apple.

I have two apple<u>s</u>.

**An apple is a naming word or <u>NOUN</u>.**
**The letter s shows that we are talking**
**about more than one <u>NOUN</u>.**

<u>**Join the words below to the correct pictures.**</u>

**tap**

**cats**

**tins**

**ant**

**pan**

**hats**

**cat**

**taps**

**ants**

**pans**

**tin**

**hat**

# Suffix

Now add the suffix S to the words below
and match to the pictures.

book + s = _____

pin + s = _____

tent + s = _____

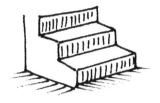

ring + s = _____

hen + s = _____

bat + s = _____

pad + s = _____

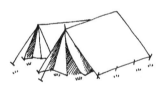

rat + s = _____

egg + s = _____

hand + s = _____

step + s = _____

cup + s = _____

ball + s = _____

# Suffix $\boxed{\textbf{S}}$ as VERB

### Look at the underlined words below. What do they all end in?

> **On Saturday Sam <u>plays</u> computer games.**
>
> **His sister Liz <u>meets</u> her friends. Their old cat Fluff <u>sleeps</u> all day.**

What kind of words are underlined?_____

When do we put suffix $\boxed{\textbf{S}}$ on these words?_____

_____

### Choose a word to complete the sentences below.
### Take care! Sometimes you will have to use suffix $\boxed{\textbf{S}}$.

e.g. My father _____ up early. *(Answer: gets)*

1   The twins _____ just like each other.

2   In the holidays I _____ to get up late.

3   Martin and his brother _____ in a band.

4   His dogs _____ in the sea.

5   My grandmother _____ five miles every day to keep fit.

6   I always _____ black coffee.

7   Mr. and Mrs. Bell _____ a tandem!

8   My dog always _____ at the postman.

9   You _____ near here, don't you?

10   In the summer they _____ to school, but in the winter their
     mother _____ them to school by car.

## KEEP FIT FRANK!

### Frank is a Keep Fit fanatic! Write sentences about what he does every day to keep fit.   e.g. He jogs in the park.

_____

_____

_____

_____

_____

_____

# Suffix $\boxed{\text{s}}$ VERB or NOUN?

**Read the passage below.**

**Underline all the words which have suffix $\boxed{\text{s}}$ .**

**Now circle the VERBS with a blue pen and the NOUNS with a red pen.**

Alfred Veryoddman has an odd name and he is an odd person. He lives in a rambling old house with many rooms, but he doesn't have a wife and children. He has a lot of pets. He keeps rabbits, goats, deer and parrots. Most people get up in the morning and go to work. But not Alfred Veryoddman! He sleeps all morning and gets up at three o'clock in the afternoon. He feeds his animals with biscuits and sweets, and he sings to them. What do you think he eats and drinks himself?

**Now write some more sentences about Alfred Veryoddman.**

_____

_____

_____

_____

_____

_____

_____

_____

_____

_____

_____

_____

_____

# Suffix  S  /s/ /z/

**Read the words below which all have the suffix  S .**

sit**s**   cap**s**   cuff**s**   act**s**

**What sound is made by the suffix  S ?**

**Now read the words below.**
**What sound does the suffix  S  make in these words?**

bed**s**   hum**s**   dig**s**   pen**s**

**In the words below  S  is a NOUN suffix.**
**Add the suffix to the base word, and write the sound in brackets.**

mat   + s = _____ (  )      pin   + s = _____ (  )

pip   + s = _____ (  )      nib   + s = _____ (  )

tab   + s = _____ (  )      clock + s = _____ (  )

pen   + s = _____ (  )      lamp  + s = _____ (  )

cliff   + s = _____ (  )      song  + s = _____ (  )

**In the words below  S  is a VERB suffix.**
**Add the suffix to the base word, and write the sound in brackets.**

stand + s = _____ (  )      cost  + s = _____ (  )

snap  + s = _____ (  )      slam  + s = _____ (  )

sprint + s = _____ (  )      pat   + s = _____ (  )

jump  + s = _____ (  )      nod   + s = _____ (  )

bend  + s = _____ (  )      run   + s = _____ (  )

# Suffix es

> When a word ends in (S) or (SS) you must
> use suffix es instead of (S).

### Add suffix es to the base words below.

cross + es = _____      bus   + es = _____

glass + es = _____      kiss  + es = _____

boss + es = _____       dress + es = _____

hiss  + es = _____      gas   + es = _____

mass + es = _____       miss  + es = _____

class + es = _____      pass  + es = _____

### Now use each word to complete the sentences below.

1  A snake _____ if it is angry.

2  If my sister _____ her driving test, she will buy a car.

3  Put the clean _____ on the top shelf.

4  The queen has a lot of beautiful _____.

5  _____ are slower than trains.

6  It is better to get ticks than _____ on your work!

7  I have _____ of homework to do this weekend.

8  How many _____ are in your school?

9  Some _____ have no colour or smell, like oxygen.

10  On the birthday card I sent love and _____.

11  My older sister always _____ me around!

12  If he _____ the bus, his father has to take him to
school.

# Suffix es

| When a word ends in (sh) you must use suffix es |
| :---: |
| instead of (s). e.g. bu<u>sh</u> es |

### Add suffix es to the base words below.

wash + es = _____          mash + es = _____

dish + es = _____          flash + es = _____

crash + es = _____          wish + es = _____

brush + es = _____          splash + es = _____

blush + es = _____          finish + es = _____

### Now use each word to complete the sentences below.

1   What would you like if you could have three _____?

2   After finishing painting, you must always wash the _____.

3   Jane always _____ when she has to read aloud in class.

4   Many people are killed each year in bad road _____.

5   He always _____ his potatoes.

6   When Tom has got his welly boots on, he always _____ in muddy puddles.

7   In many schools the last lesson _____ at 3.30 p.m.

8   During the thunderstorm the sky was lit up by _____ of lightning.

9   Her husband always _____ the _____ after Sunday lunch.

# Suffix es

> ## Words ending in (x) also take suffix es
> ## instead of (s). e.g. bo<u>x</u> es

**Find 10 words in the word-square below ending in (X).**

**Add suffix es and use each word to complete the sentences below.**

*(Words go ACROSS and DOWN only.)*

| d | r | e | f | l | e | x | v |
|---|---|---|---|---|---|---|---|
| o | s | i | x | m | f | a | x |
| r | f | k | b | o | x | w | e |
| e | o | r | m | y | f | i | x |
| l | x | a | i | d | j | c | p |
| a | l | h | x | t | a | x | s |
| x | b | s | u | f | f | i | x |

b _ _
f _ _
f _ _
f _ _
m _ _
r _ _ _ _ _ _
r _ _ _ _
s _ _
s _ _ _ _ _
t _ _

1  Nobody likes to pay _____.

2  Last night I saw a family of _____ in my garden.

3  How many _____ make sixty?

4  If you have good _____, you react quickly.

5  A plumber _____ broken pipes.

6  _____ are endings on words.

7  Red _____ with yellow to make orange.

8  If you want to send _____, you need a fax machine.

9  My mother _____ by reading books.

10  Five _____ of books were found in the attic.

23

# Suffix es

---

**Words ending in (ch) also take suffix es**
**instead of (s).** e.g. bran<u>ch</u> es

<u>Find 9 words in the word-square below ending in (ch).</u>
<u>Add suffix es and use each word to complete the sentences below.</u>
*(Words go ACROSS and DOWN only.)*

| d | n | j | t | e | a | c | h |
|---|---|---|---|---|---|---|---|
| l | b | e | n | c | h | o | f |
| c | h | u | r | c | h | a | r |
| r | e | s | b | u | n | c | h |
| u | l | p | e | a | c | h | k |
| t | l | u | n | c | h | q | x |
| c | g | v | c | a | t | c | h |
| h | t | o | t | y | m | u | w |

_____

_____

_____

_____

_____

_____

_____

_____

_____

1  I love _____ and cream.

2  We needed ten _____ for the outing to London.

3  The _____ in the park were full of people eating
   picnic _____.

4  My father _____ French and Spanish.

5  If you break a leg, you will have to use _____.

6  _____ of ripe bananas hung from the trees.

7  Many _____ have graveyards.

8  My brother never _____ a cold.

---

# Suffix es

The suffix es is used instead of (s) when
the base word ends in:

(-x), (-s), (-ss), (-sh) or (-ch).

Examples are given below.

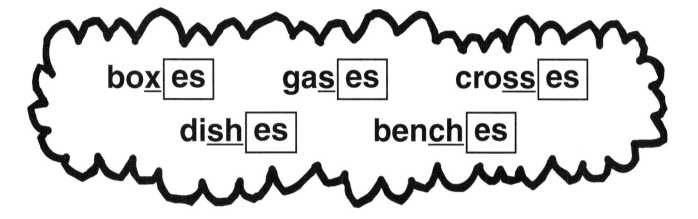

Add the suffix **es** to the base words below.

| | | | | |
|---|---|---|---|---|
| 1 | bus | _____ | 9 class | _____ |
| 2 | fox | _____ | 10 trench | _____ |
| 3 | church | _____ | 11 dress | _____ |
| 4 | brush | _____ | 12 fish | _____ |
| 5 | coach | _____ | 13 miss | _____ |
| 6 | tax | _____ | 14 hiss | _____ |
| 7 | bunch | _____ | 15 wash | _____ |
| 8 | six | _____ | 16 bless | _____ |

# Suffix es

**A.** **Circle the suffixes in the words below.**

**Each word ends in suffix s or es .**

| | | | |
|---|---|---|---|
| hopes | boxes | books | taxis |
| prefixes | lines | crosses | gates |
| gifts | lives | stitches | ties |
| divers | trees | bunches | switches |

**B.** **Add the correct suffix to the words below to make them plural in meaning.**

1 raft _____

2 desk _____

3 tax _____

4 park _____

5 splash _____

6 wish _____

7 class _____

8 speech _____

9 wasp _____

10 risk _____

11 brush _____

12 vest _____

13 quilt _____

14 ditch _____

15 fox _____

16 sink _____

17 kiss _____

18 crisp _____

19 sketch _____

20 fist _____

# Suffix es or s : Words ending in 'y'

---

## Rule

**When a word ends in 'y', look at the letter <u>before</u> the 'y' in the base word.**

**If this letter is a <u>VOWEL</u>, <u>JUST ADD</u> suffix s .**

e.g. pla<u>y</u> + s = plays.

**If the letter before 'y' is a <u>CONSONANT</u>, <u>CHANGE</u> 'y' to 'i' and add suffix es .**

e.g. jel<u>l</u>y + es = jell<u>i</u>es.

---

<u>**Write the plural of the nouns below by following the rules above.**</u>

| | | | |
|---|---|---|---|
| monkey | _____ | essay | _____ |
| baby | _____ | story | _____ |
| dolly | _____ | puppy | _____ |
| day | _____ | valley | _____ |
| jelly | _____ | cherry | _____ |
| party | _____ | bay | _____ |
| tray | _____ | joy | _____ |
| boy | _____ | country | _____ |
| candy | _____ | lady | _____ |
| ruby | _____ | journey | _____ |

---

# Suffix es or s : Nouns and verbs ending in 'y'

## Find 10 NOUNS ending in 'y' in the word-square below.
## Write out each word and then make it plural by following the correct rule. *(Words go ACROSS and DOWN only.)*

| b | a | t | t | e | r | y | o |
|---|---|---|---|---|---|---|---|
| g | e | j | o | c | k | e | y |
| d | a | e | h | o | b | b | y |
| o | r | r | p | e | n | n | y |
| n | m | s | o | i | l | c | k |
| k | y | e | n | t | r | a | y |
| e | r | y | y | o | n | s | v |
| y | m | b | q | y | f | d | h |

**Noun Singular**        **Plural**

a __ __ __        _____

b __ __ __ __ __        _____

d __ __ __ __ __        _____

h __ __ __ __        _____

j __ __ __ __ __        _____

j __ __ __ __        _____

p __ __ __ __        _____

p __ __ __ __        _____

t __ __        _____

t __ __ __        _____

## Find 10 VERBS ending in 'y' in the word-square below.
## Write out each word and then add suffix S , or CHANGE 'y' to 'i' and add suffix es .

| a | r | e | p | l | y | h | d |
|---|---|---|---|---|---|---|---|
| k | t | e | m | p | l | o | y |
| p | l | a | y | c | s | l | b |
| w | o | r | r | y | t | v | a |
| b | t | i | e | r | u | g | n |
| u | r | b | u | y | d | w | n |
| r | y | f | s | m | y | x | o |
| y | j | u | e | n | j | o | y |

**Verb**        **Verb + ending**

a __ __ __ __        _____

b __ __ __        _____

b __ __        _____

e __ __ __ __ __        _____

e __ __ __ __        _____

p __ __ __        _____

r __ __ __ __        _____

s __ __ __ __        _____

t __ __ __        _____

w __ __ __ __ __        _____

# Suffix es

Some words which end in '<u>o</u>' take suffix es instead of (s).

### Add es to the words below.

g<u>o</u> + es = _____          d<u>o</u> + es = _____

### Now use each word in a sentence of your own.

_____

_____

### Unscramble the 10 words below which end in 'o'. Then add suffix es to make each word plural.

*(The meanings and first letters have been given to help you.)*

**o a l v o c n**  An exploding mountain.                    v _____
                   Plural = _____

**h o e c**        This comes back to you!                  e _____
                   Plural = _____

**o o t t m a**    A red fruit used in salads.              t _____
                   Plural = _____

**o i o n d m**    An oblong piece used in a game.          d _____
                   Plural = _____

**e h o r**        A brave person in real life or in a book.  h _____
                   Plural = _____

**a o m n g**      A delicious tropical fruit.              m _____
                   Plural = _____

**f u l f a o b**  A kind of ox.                            b _____
                   Plural = _____

**a r o c g**      What a boat carries.                     c _____
                   Plural = _____

**o t o t p a**    A common vegetable.                      p _____
                   Plural = _____

**o d r t a o n**  A violent storm.                         t _____
                   Plural = _____

# Suffix ing

---

**The suffix ing is used as a verb ending to describe what is happening now.**

e.g. What is Sunil do<u>ing</u>?   He is kick<u>ing</u> the ball.

---

**Add ing to the words below. Use a red pen.**

smell_____        cry_____        push_____

sing_____        wash_____        jump_____

**Now use each word to complete the sentences below.**

1    The boy is _____ over the box.

2    Kumar is _____ his hands.

3    The children are _____.

4    The little girl is _____ the flower.

5    Mr. Bell is _____ his car.

6    The baby is _____.

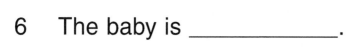

---

# Suffix ing

### Add ing to the words below.

stand_____    fall_____    climb_____    eat_____

play_____    drink_____    bark_____    fly_____

### Now use each word to write a sentence about the pictures below.

# Adding ing to base words: DOUBLING

**Look at the words below.**

wag     step     sit     hop     run

They are all short words with **one** beat.
They all have **one** short vowel in the middle.
They all end in **one** consonant.

We can mark this pattern like this: **wǎĝ**

**Now mark the pattern for the other words in the box.**

## Rule

**When we add suffix ing to words with this pattern, we must DOUBLE the last letter of the base word.**

e.g. wǎg + ǐng = wagging

**Add suffix ing to the base words below. Remember to follow the DOUBLING rule.**

1  cut   + ing = _____

2  beg   + ing = _____

3  run   + ing = _____

4  mop   + ing = _____

5  slam  + ing = _____

6  nod   + ing = _____

7  spin  + ing = _____

8  step  + ing = _____

9  win   + ing = _____

10  grab  + ing = _____

11  rob   + ing = _____

12  dig   + ing = _____

# Adding ing to base words: DOUBLING

**Add suffix ing to the base words below. Remember to follow the DOUBLING rule.**

shop + ing = _____          drip + ing = _____

flap + ing = _____          sob + ing = _____

get + ing = _____          skip + ing = _____

jog + ing = _____          chat + ing = _____

wag + ing = _____          swim + ing = _____

pop + ing = _____          chop + ing = _____

**Now use each of the words you have made to complete the sentences below.**

1  "The tap is _____. Go and turn it off."

2  My sister is _____ married next week.

3  The teacher told us to stop _____ and get on with our work.

4  The dog started _____ its tail when I patted it.

5  The man was _____ wood with an axe.

6  I made a _____ list before I went to the supermarket.

7  The flag was _____ in the wind.

8  The little boy who had lost his mother was _____.

9  "Do you like _____ in the sea?"

10  My father goes _____ every day to keep fit.

11  The children were _____ in the playground.

12  "I am just _____ out to get some milk."

# Adding ing to base words: DROP 'e'

## Rule

**When we add suffix ing to words which end in 'e',
we must DROP the 'e' of the base word.**

e.g. write + ing = writing.

### Add suffix ing to the base words below.

smoke + ing = _____     skate + ing = _____

use + ing = _____     ride + ing = _____

cycle + ing = _____     escape + ing = _____

freeze + ing = _____     shine + ing = _____

hide + ing = _____     dine + ing = _____

confuse + ing = _____     drive + ing = _____

### Now use each word to complete the sentences below.

1  My hobbies are ice-_____ and horse-_____.

2  After _____ from the zoo, the monkey was found
   _____ in the park.

3  _____ a computer for the first time can be
   very _____.

4  The sun was _____ brightly, but it was still
   _____ cold.

5  There was a 'NO _____' sign in the _____
   room.

6  If the traffic is bad, _____ to work may be quicker
   than _____.

# Adding ing to base words ending in 'y'

## Rule

**When we add suffix ing to a base word ending in 'y', we JUST ADD the suffix.**

e.g.    cry + ing = crying.

apply + ing = applying.

### Add suffix ing to the base words below.

decay + ing = _____          annoy + ing = _____

enjoy + ing = _____          sway   + ing = _____

apply + ing = _____          rely    + ing = _____

spray + ing = _____          study  + ing = _____

worry + ing = _____          marry + ing = _____

### Now use each word to complete the sentences below.

1  My brother is _____ a girl he met on holiday, and I am going to be a bridesmaid.

2  I am _____ on you to help me.

3  The trees were _____ in the strong wind.

4  I am _____ for a job in London.

5  If a tooth is _____, the dentist will fill it or take it out.

6  The children were _____ themselves on the beach making sand castles.

7  It is very _____ to run to the bus-stop and then miss the bus by a few seconds!

8  The elephant was _____ water over itself with its trunk.

9  Stop _____! Here is your missing passport.

10  My sister is _____ English at Oxford University.

# Adding ing to base words

Add the suffix ing to the base words below.
Follow the correct rule: DOUBLE, DROP 'e' or JUST ADD.

## TEST ONE

1 phone + ing = _____

2 grip + ing = _____

3 spy + ing = _____

4 slide + ing = _____

5 hit + ing = _____

6 wipe + ing = _____

7 bet + ing = _____

8 weed + ing = _____

9 flame + ing = _____

10 wait + ing = _____

11 advise + ing = _____

12 pray + ing = _____

13 strut + ing = _____

14 drag + ing = _____

15 shout + ing = _____

## TEST TWO

1 snap + ing = _____

2 fry + ing = _____

3 shake + ing = _____

4 swim + ing = _____

5 feel + ing = _____

6 tug + ing = _____

7 speed + ing = _____

8 sleep + ing = _____

9 waste + ing = _____

10 clean + ing = _____

11 live + ing = _____

12 hurry + ing = _____

13 drop + ing = _____

14 shut + ing = _____

15 choose + ing = _____

Score _____
15

Score _____
15

# Suffix **ed**

---

The suffix **ed** is put on the end of <u>VERBS</u> to show that something happened in the past.
It shows <u>PAST TENSE</u>.

    e.g.   Yesterday I walk<u>ed</u> to school.

          Last week I watch<u>ed</u> a good film.

<u>Write down 5 things you did yesterday and 5 things you did last week.</u>

## YESTERDAY

_____

_____

_____

_____

_____

## LAST WEEK

_____

_____

_____

_____

_____

<u>Underline all the VERBS in your sentences.</u>

<u>How many of them needed the</u> **ed** <u>suffix?</u>

<u>Now open your reading book at any page.</u>

<u>How many words can you see which have suffix</u> **ed** ?

---

# Suffix ed

---

> ## The suffix ed as past tense ending
> ## is often found in stories.

**Read the beginning of the story below.**
**Underline all the verbs which have the suffix ed .**

It was a dark and stormy night. The wind roared and the tall pine trees in the forest swayed dangerously. They moaned and creaked as if they were in pain. In the distance, thunder rumbled and flashes of lightning lit up the night sky. The old man stumbled along the forest track. He had come a long way and had little strength left. He wanted to lie down, curl up like an animal and sleep. But there was no turning back now.

At last he spotted a dim light ahead. He gathered his strength and headed towards it. It was a small wooden house in a forest clearing. With a trembling hand he knocked on the front door. There was no reply. He waited and listened, and then knocked again. No reply. He slowly lifted the latch and pushed the door open. A dark shadow moved across the wall in front of him. He stepped inside and closed the door.

**Now continue the story in your exercise book.**

## Who is the old man?

## Why has he come to the house in the forest?

## Who or what was inside?

## What happened next?

## When you have finished, give your story a title.

---

# Suffix ed /t/ /d/ /id/

> The suffix ed is added to base words to show
> the past tense form of the verb.
>
> It can have 3 sounds:
>
> kick**ed** /t/       fill**ed** /d/       mend**ed** /id/

**Add the ed suffix to the words below and write the sound in brackets.**

stay + ed = _____ (  )     miss + ed = _____ (  )

sniff + ed = _____ (  )     yell + ed = _____ (  )

tramp + ed = _____ (  )     block + ed = _____ (  )

pull + ed = _____ (  )     pass + ed = _____ (  )

dent + ed = _____ (  )     insist + ed = _____ (  )

drill + ed = _____ (  )     stamp + ed = _____ (  )

hand + ed = _____ (  )     act + ed = _____ (  )

pick + ed = _____ (  )     stuff + ed = _____ (  )

intend + ed = _____ (  )     peel + ed = _____ (  )

test + ed = _____ (  )     block + ed = _____ (  )

lift + ed = _____ (  )     long + ed = _____ (  )

pinch + ed = _____ (  )     thank + ed = _____ (  )

# Suffix ed

**Match the words below to the correct picture.**

**Listen to the sound of the suffix ed .**

**Put the sound in brackets below each picture. /t/ /d/ or /id/.**

| jumped | closed | reminded | (cooked) |
|--------|--------|----------|----------|
| kicked | hunted | counted | rested |
| dived | shouted | filled | asked |
| | shaved | mended | splashed |

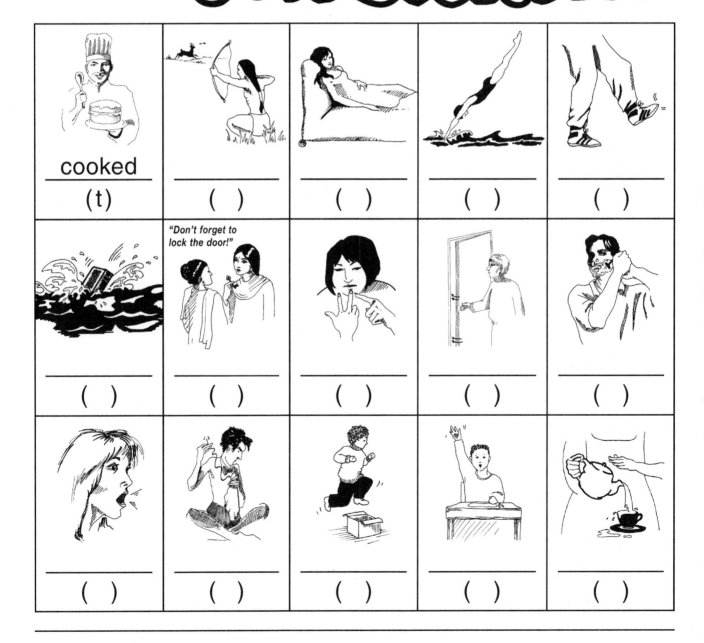

| cooked | | | | |
|--------|--------|--------|--------|--------|
| (t) | ( ) | ( ) | ( ) | ( ) |
| ( ) | ( ) | ( ) | ( ) | ( ) |
| ( ) | ( ) | ( ) | ( ) | ( ) |

# Suffix ⬛ed on words ending in (ll), (ss), and (ff).

## Add ed to the words below. Use a red pen.

| (ll) words | (ss) words | (ff) words |
|---|---|---|
| yell_____ | miss_____ | sniff_____ |
| pull_____ | pass_____ | stuff_____ |
| fill_____ | dress_____ | huff_____ |
| drill_____ | hiss_____ | puff_____ |
| grill_____ | cross_____ | |
| thrill_____ | impress_____ | |

## Now use each word to complete the sentences below.

1   The dentist _____ my tooth before he _____ it.

2   I quickly _____ the road when I saw the bus coming, but I just _____ it.

3   I was _____ when I _____ my driving test first time.

4   Everybody _____ and _____ as they went up the steep hill.

5   When the snake lifted its head and _____, I _____ out in fright!

6   The dog _____ the bone greedily, and then _____ it out of the plastic bag with its teeth.

7   For lunch we ate _____ fish with _____ peppers.

8   His parents were very _____ to see him _____ so smartly for his job interview, as they had never seen him in a suit or tie!

# Suffix $\boxed{\textbf{ed}}$ on words ending in $\widehat{\text{nd}}$, $\widehat{\text{nt}}$, and $\widehat{\text{mp}}$.

## Add $\boxed{\text{ed}}$ to the words below. Use a red pen.

| $\widehat{\text{nd}}$ words | $\widehat{\text{nt}}$ words | $\widehat{\text{mp}}$ words |
|---|---|---|
| intend_____ | print_____ | stamp_____ |
| strand_____ | glint_____ | clamp_____ |
| attend_____ | faint_____ | bump_____ |
| hand_____ | pant_____ | dump_____ |
| end_____ | want_____ | camp_____ |

## Now use each word to complete the sentences below.

1 The tall man _____ his head on the low doorway.

2 A lot of people _____ the meeting which finally _____ at 9 p.m.

3 The man at the desk _____ my passport and then _____ it back to me.

4 The gold coin _____ in the man's hand.

5 The woman nearly _____ when she saw that her car had been wheel-_____ because she had parked it on double yellow lines.

6 Tom was _____ when he missed the last bus home.

7 The scouts _____ on the hilltop, although they had _____ to camp lower down in the valley.

8 A big pile of _____ papers had been _____ in the dustbin.

9 The dog _____ because it _____ a drink.

# Suffix ed on words ending in ck

Find 15 words ending in ck in the word-square.

Add ed suffix to these words and use each one to complete the sentences below. *(Words go ACROSS and DOWN only.)*

| s | t | a | c | k | l | o | c | k |
|---|---|---|---|---|---|---|---|---|
| b | i | s | t | r | i | c | k | b |
| j | c | p | r | i | c | k | s | l |
| m | k | i | c | k | f | v | f | o |
| l | i | c | k | o | c | w | b | c |
| p | a | c | k | s | h | o | c | k |
| i | e | u | d | p | e | c | k | l |
| c | x | q | u | a | c | k | y | g |
| k | s | m | a | c | k | n | h | q |

b _ _ _ _       p _ _ _ _ _

c _ _ _ _ _     q _ _ _ _ _

k _ _ _        s _ _ _ _ _

l _ _ _ _      s _ _ _ _ _

l _ _ _       s _ _ _ _ _

p _ _ _        t _ _ _

p _ _ _        t _ _ _ _ _

p _ _ _

1   She _____ her bags and left home.

2   The hens _____ at the corn.

3   They had to call the plumber because the sink was _____.

4   Ahmed _____ the ball high into the air.

5   James was proud to be _____ for the school team.

6   Before leaving home, he _____ that he had his passport.

7   The little girl _____ her ice-cream happily.

8   She _____ the door before going to bed.

9   The books were _____ in a neat pile on the teacher's desk.

10  On April 1st, Sam _____ his mother into thinking she had won the lottery!

11  The little boy _____ his baby sister in a temper tantrum.

12  The teacher _____ all the correct answers.

13  The ducks _____ noisily when bread was thrown to them.

14  George was _____ to get only 20% for his Maths test.

15  She _____ her finger on the sharp needle.

# Adding ed to base words: DOUBLING

## Rule

**When adding suffix ed to a base word with one syllable, one short vowel and one consonant at the end, we must DOUBLE the final consonant of the base word.**

e.g.    slĭp + ĕd = slipped.

hŭm + ĕd = hummed.

### Look at the word-sums below. Circle the 10 which double.

| | | |
|---|---|---|
| drag + ed | peel + ed | dream + ed |
| boat + ed | jog + ed | fool + ed |
| dump + ed | trim + ed | weed + ed |
| snap + ed | sprain + ed | zip + ed |
| shout + ed | ask + ed | hop + ed |
| rip + ed | bang + ed | hoot + ed |
| roam + ed | grip + ed | heal + ed |
| seem + ed | fail + ed | flip + ed |
| swig + ed | load + ed | heap + ed |

# Adding ed to base words: DROP 'e'

## Rule

**When we add suffix ed to words which end in 'e', we must DROP the 'e' of the base word.**

e.g. hopé + ěd = hoped.

### Add suffix ed to the base words below.

phone + ed = _____       close + ed = _____

wave + ed = _____       stroke + ed = _____

stare + ed = _____       invite + ed = _____

smile + ed = _____       sneeze + ed = _____

rescue + ed = _____       move + ed = _____

live + ed = _____       dive + ed = _____

### Now use each of the words you have made to complete the sentences below.

1  The little boy _____ as he _____ the dog.

2  As Rachel _____ the garden gate, she turned round and _____ goodbye to her mother.

3  Mike _____ his girlfriend and _____ her to the cinema.

4  The brave man _____ into the canal and _____ the child who had fallen in.

5  The family _____ in London for ten years, and then they _____ to York.

6  When Amit _____ very loudly in class, everybody _____ at him, and the teacher was cross!

# Adding ed to base words ending in (ay), (ey), or (oy).

## Rule

**When we add suffix ed to a base word ending in (ay), (ey) or (oy), we JUST ADD the suffix.**

e.g.    st<u>ay</u> + ed = stayed.

surv<u>ey</u> + ed = surveyed.

empl<u>oy</u> + ed = employed.

### Add suffix ed to the base words below.

destroy + ed = _____          display + ed = _____

annoy  + ed = _____          journey + ed = _____

spray  + ed = _____          decay  + ed = _____

obey   + ed = _____          pray   + ed = _____

curtsey + ed = _____          enjoy  + ed = _____

### Now use each word to complete the sentences below.

1   The farmer _____ his crops with weed-killer.

2   The parents _____ watching their children in the play.

3   Many wonderful goods were _____ in the shop windows.

4   The little girl _____ to the queen and gave her a bunch of flowers.

5   Most of the city was _____ in the earthquake.

6   Sinbad the Sailor _____ to many strange and exciting lands.

7   The vicar _____ that there would be peace in the world.

8   The dog _____ its master and always came when called.

9   The dentist took out the tooth which had _____ badly.

10  I was _____ to find that I had just missed the bus.

# Adding ed to base words

**Add the suffix ed to the base words below.**

**Follow the correct rule: DOUBLE, DROP 'e' or JUST ADD.**

## TEST ONE

1  shave + ed = _____

2  step   + ed = _____

3  dream + ed = _____

4  yap    + ed = _____

5  brag   + ed = _____

6  advise + ed = _____

7  obey   + ed = _____

8  brood + ed = _____

9  flop    + ed = _____

10  waste + ed = _____

11  blaze + ed = _____

12  strap + ed = _____

13  need  + ed = _____

14  betray + ed = _____

15  plod   + ed = _____

## TEST TWO

1  heap   + ed = _____

2  trot    + ed = _____

3  wade   + ed = _____

4  ban    + ed = _____

5  strip   + ed = _____

6  train   + ed = _____

7  enjoy  + ed = _____

8  behave + ed = _____

9  thud   + ed = _____

10  peel   + ed = _____

11  rule   + ed = _____

12  chug   + ed = _____

13  bake   + ed = _____

14  spray  + ed = _____

15  trade  + ed = _____

Score _____          Score _____

15                                    15

# Suffix | y |

| Suffix | y | changes a noun or verb into an **ADJECTIVE**. |
e.g. lucky number.
itchy nose. |

**Add suffix | y | to the base words below. Use a red pen.**
**Choose a suitable NOUN to follow each adjective with suffix | y |.**

e.g. **ADJECTIVE   NOUN**
springy    mattress

| **ADJECTIVE**<br>**with suffix 'y'** | **NOUN** | **ADJECTIVE**<br>**with suffix 'y'** | **NOUN** |
|---|---|---|---|
| stick__ | _____ | risk__ | _____ |
| mess__ | _____ | oil__ | _____ |
| rust__ | _____ | spook__ | _____ |
| sleep__ | _____ | fuss__ | _____ |
| boss__ | _____ | greed__ | _____ |
| bush__ | _____ | curl__ | _____ |
| grass__ | _____ | milk__ | _____ |

**Many weather words end in suffix | y |.**
e.g. sunny, foggy.

**Find 9 weather words in the word-square to which you can add**
**suffix | y |. Add the suffix and write out the complete word.**
*(Words go ACROSS and DOWN only.)*

| d | c | l | o | u | d | c |
|---|---|---|---|---|---|---|
| s | t | o | r | m | f | s |
| r | a | i | n | b | r | h |
| m | h | j | a | e | o | o |
| i | w | i | n | d | s | w |
| s | n | o | w | q | t | e |
| t | h | u | n | d | e | r |

c _ _ _ _    + y = _____
f _ _ _ _    + y = _____
m _ _ _    + y = _____
r _ _ _    + y = _____
s _ _ _ _ _    + y = _____
s _ _ _    + y = _____
s _ _ _ _    + y = _____
t _ _ _ _ _ _    + y = _____
w _ _ _    + y = _____

48

# Suffix y

---

## Rule

**Suffix y is a <u>VOWEL</u> suffix, so we may have to follow the <u>DOUBLE</u> or <u>DROP 'e'</u> rule.**

e.g.   mŭd + y̆ = mu<u>dd</u>y.

ic<u>e</u> + y̆ = icy.

---

### Add suffix y to the base words below.
### Follow the correct rule: DOUBLE, DROP 'e' or JUST ADD.

greed  + y = _____        fat      + y = _____

fleece + y = _____        shade  + y = _____

gloom + y = _____        wobble + y = _____

shake  + y = _____        frost    + y = _____

skin    + y = _____        fog      + y = _____

sleep  + y = _____        health  + y = _____

### Now use each word to complete the sentences below.

1   My handwriting was _____ because I was writing on
    a table with _____ legs.

2   It is not _____ to eat too many _____ foods.

3   The _____ dog ate everything it could find, but it was
    still as _____ as a rake.

4   On _____ days, everything looks dark and _____.

5   He felt _____ after walking for 2 hours in the hot sun, so
    he sat down in a _____ spot and had a nap.

6   I always wear my _____ jacket on cold, _____
    mornings.

---

# Suffix y

Unscramble the base words below and then add suffix y to get an
ADJECTIVE which describes a person.
Follow the correct suffixing rule: DOUBLE, DROP 'e' or JUST ADD.

| Meaning | Base word | Answer |
|---|---|---|
| e.g. This person likes to be in charge | o b s s + y = | bossy |

This person is very clever.                         a b i n r + y = _____

This person likes to answer back.                   h k e c e + y = _____

Don't ask this person to do any work.               a l z e      + y = _____

This person is not quiet.                            i n s e o + y = _____

This person eats a lot.                              e g e d r + y = _____

This person is a bit sly.                            r t a c f + y = _____

This person might not speak to you.                  u k l s      + y = _____

This person is clever with words.                    i w t        + y = _____

This person likes to talk a lot.                     t c a h      + y = _____

This person is probably in one or
more of the school teams.                            t s r o p + y = _____

This person likes to know other
people's business.                                   e o n s      + y = _____

This person gets worked up about
small things.                                        s u s f      + y = _____

This person does not tidy up.                        s e m s      + y = _____

This person makes you laugh.                         n f u        + y = _____

# Suffix ful

| The suffix ful added to the end of base words means 'full of'. e.g. a cup<u>ful</u> of milk. |
|---|

### Write words with ful below each picture.

an _____ of books      a _____ of pins      a _____ of sugar

a _____ of shopping      a _____ of water      a _____ of money

### Choose 2 from the list below and draw pictures in the boxes.
### Fill in the missing words below the pictures.

a boxful of toys      a bagful of sweets      a glassful of water

a spadeful of sand      a bottleful of Coke      a plateful of food

a _____ of _____      a _____ of _____

51

# Suffix ful

The suffix **ful** is added to base words to mean 'full of'.
It changes a **NOUN** into an **ADJECTIVE**.

e.g. colour<u>ful</u> sunset.

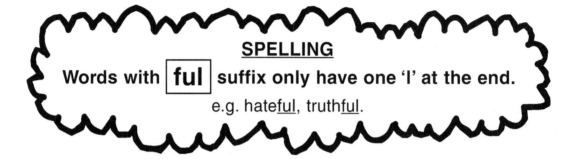

**SPELLING**

Words with **ful** suffix only have one 'l' at the end.

e.g. hate<u>ful</u>, truth<u>ful</u>.

**QUIZ: Find the word with ful which completes each sentence.**
**The first letter has been given to help you.**

1   A ballerina is very g _ _ _ _ _ _ _.

2   A swollen ankle is very p _ _ _ _ _ _.

3   Smoking is h _ _ _ _ _ _ to your health.

4   Living in the countryside is more p _ _ _ _ _ _ _ than in a busy city.

5   A hammer is a very u _ _ _ _ _ tool.

6   The f _ _ _ _ _ _ _ _ boy could never remember what he needed
    to bring to school each day.

7   Despite her illness, she was always bright and c _ _ _ _ _ _ _.

8   We had a w _ _ _ _ _ _ _ _ holiday in Spain last year.

**Now write your own sentences for the words below.**

**thankful     spiteful     helpful     faithful     restful**

_____

_____

_____

_____

_____

_____

# Suffix less

> The suffix **less** is added to base words to mean
> 'without'. It changes a **NOUN** into an **ADJECTIVE**.
> e.g. moon<u>less</u> night.

**Add suffix** **less** **to the base words below. Use a red pen.**
**Then use each one to complete the sentences below.**

| | | | |
|---|---|---|---|
| help____ | care____ | rest____ | cloud____ |
| sleep____ | hope____ | end____ | taste____ |
| home____ | leaf____ | seed____ | worth____ |

1  The _____ child kept walking around the room.

2  The ring looked expensive, but in fact it was _____.

3  She felt very tired after a _____ night.

4  _____ people sometimes have to sleep on the streets.

5  The _____ boy spilt ink all over his book.

6  A baby is _____ when it is born.

7  Peter was good at Maths, but he was _____ at spelling.

8  The last lesson of the day seemed _____ to the children.

9  In winter the trees are bare and _____.

10  The sun was shining from a _____ sky.

11  I always buy _____ grapes.

12  The meal looked delicious, but the meat was _____.

# Suffix **less**

Join the suffix **less** to the words below.
Then write one NOUN which can follow the adjective with 'less'.

| | ADJECTIVE | NOUN |
|---|---|---|
| e.g. cord + less = | cord<u>less</u> | telephone |

|  |  | ADJECTIVE | NOUN |
|---|---|---|---|
| 1 | breath + less = | _____ | _____ |
| 2 | colour + less = | _____ | _____ |
| 3 | power + less = | _____ | _____ |
| 4 | motion + less = | _____ | _____ |
| 5 | noise + less = | _____ | _____ |
| 6 | thought + less = | _____ | _____ |
| 7 | shape + less = | _____ | _____ |
| 8 | pain + less = | _____ | _____ |
| 9 | leaf + less = | _____ | _____ |
| 10 | harm + less = | _____ | _____ |
| 11 | use + less = | _____ | _____ |
| 12 | price + less = | _____ | _____ |

### Look at the base words from the above exercise.
### Which 6 words can also take suffix **ful**?

_____ + ful = _____

_____ + ful = _____

_____ + ful = _____

_____ + ful = _____

_____ + ful = _____

_____ + ful = _____

**Can you think of any more word pairs like this?**

# Suffix ness

---

The suffix **ness** is added to base words which are **ADJECTIVES** and it makes the word into a **NOUN**. It describes a state, quality or feeling. This type of noun is called an **ABSTRACT** noun because you can't touch or see it.

|  **ADJECTIVE** | | **NOUN** |
|---|---|---|
| e.g. dark + | ness = | dark<u>ness</u> |

**Add suffix** **ness** **to the base words below.**
**Note that if the base word ends in 'n', you will end up with 'nn'**
**in the middle of the word.**

e.g. gree<u>n</u> + <u>n</u>ess = gree**nn**ess

bright   + ness = _____     fond   + ness = _____

mad     + ness = _____     sad    + ness = _____

blunt   + ness = _____     mean + ness = _____

sudden + ness = _____     shy    + ness = _____

fresh    + ness = _____     rude   + ness = _____

### Now use each word to complete the sentences below.

1   His parents often told him off because of his _____.

2   The _____ of the knife made it useless.

3   The old lady had a great _____ for cats.

4   If you get up early you can enjoy the _____ of the air.

5   The little boy didn't like parties because of his _____.

6   We could see clearly by the _____ of the moon.

7   Nobody liked the old man because of his _____.

8   The _____ of the man's death gave everybody a shock.

9   Some people think it is _____ to do bunjee jumping!

10   The child's brown eyes were full of _____.

---

# Adding ful , less or ness to base words

## Rule

The suffixes ful , less and ness all begin with a **CONSONANT**, so in most cases we **JUST ADD** to the base word.

e.g.   sin + ful    = sinful.
hope + less  = hopeless.
red + ness  = redness.

But if a base word ends in 'y', we must **CHANGE 'y' to 'i'** if we add ful , less or ness .

e.g.   beauty + ful   = beautiful.
pity + less   = pitiless.
dusty + ness  = dustiness.

One syllable words ending in 'y' do **not** change 'y' to 'i'.

e.g.   shy + ness  = shyness.

### Add the suffixes to the base words below.
### Follow the correct rule: JUST ADD, or CHANGE 'y' to 'i'.

penny   + less = _____        plenty   + ful = _____

fret    + ful = _____        rude    + ness = _____

pretty  + ness = _____        care    + less = _____

cheer   + ful = _____        duty    + ful = _____

cool    + ness = _____        dry     + ness = _____

mercy   + ful = _____        smoke   + less = _____

happy   + ness = _____        taste   + ful = _____

drunken + ness = _____        seed    + less = _____

sorrow  + ful = _____        noise   + less = _____

# Suffixes ful , less and ness

**Add suffix ful , less or ness to complete the words in the sentences below.**

1 Helen Keller was a wonder_____ woman who led a success_____ life despite the double handicap of deaf_____ and blind_____.

2 The hard_____ of the bunk bed gave her a sleep_____ night, leading to tired_____ the next day.

3 We were all grate_____ for the kind_____ and friendli_____ that we were shown.

4 The fear_____ child was afraid of dark_____.

5 When we looked down the well it seemed bottom_____, and its inky black_____ made us shudder.

6 The man was so forget_____ and thought_____ that he even forgot his wife's birthday.

7 If you are job_____ and home_____, it leads to a feeling of hopeless_____.

8 The spite_____ child lost friends because of his mean_____ and nasti_____.

## Adding 2 suffixes to a base word.

**Do the word-sums below to create a new word with 2 suffixes.**

cheer + ful + ness = _____

rest + less + ness = _____

use + ful + ness = _____

sleep + less + ness = _____

hope + ful + ness = _____

forget + ful + ness = _____

home + less + ness = _____

care + less + ness = _____

play + ful + ness = _____

# Suffix  ly

The suffix  ly  is added to **ADJECTIVES** to make them **ADVERBS**.

An **ADVERB** tells us more about the verb.

**VERB**

e.g. The man walked down the road.

**(No extra information is given about the verb.)**

**VERB   ADVERB**

The man walked quickly down the road.

**(The ADVERB 'quickly' tells us how the man walked.)**

**Fill in the missing vowels in the adverbs below.**
**(Use a dictionary if you are not sure of the spelling.)**

s_fely      nerv_ _sly      qu_ _tly      impr_ss_vely      s_ftly

(un)st_ _dily      h_ngrily      sk_lf_lly      (im)pat_ _ntly

qu_ckly      r_ckl_ssly      p_l_tely      acc_r_tely      (un)t_dily

c_r_fully      n_ _tly      cas_ _lly      gr_ _dily      s_ns_bly

h_ppily      br_skly      int_ll_g_ntly      c_r_lessly      sl_wly

conf_dently      thor_ _ghly      d_nger_ _sly      n_ _sily

cr_ftily      r_dely      b_ldly      m_ssily      l_zily      sm_rtly

sw_ftly      s_lently      f_rmly      el_g_ntly      scr_ffily

**Now choose from the list above and write 4 ADVERBS which can go**
**with the verbs below.**

| VERB | ADVERBS | | | |
|------|---------|--|--|--|
| walk | _____ | _____ | _____ | _____ |
| work | _____ | _____ | _____ | _____ |
| speak | _____ | _____ | _____ | _____ |
| drive | _____ | _____ | _____ | _____ |
| dress | _____ | _____ | _____ | _____ |
| play | _____ | _____ | _____ | _____ |
| eat | _____ | _____ | _____ | _____ |

# Adding ly to base words

## Rule

**The suffix ly is a <u>CONSONANT</u> suffix, so in most cases we <u>JUST ADD</u> to base words.**

e.g.   rude + ly = rudely.

slow + ly = slowly.

**But if the base word ends in 'y', we must CHANGE '<u>y</u>' to '<u>i</u>' before adding the suffix ly.**

e.g.   happ<u>y</u> + ly = happ<u>i</u>ly.

<u>**Add suffix ly to the base words below by following the correct rule:**</u>
<u>**JUST ADD or CHANGE 'y' to 'i'.**</u>

safe      + ly = _____         polite    + ly = _____

greedy    + ly = _____         skilful   + ly = _____

selfish   + ly = _____         rude      + ly = _____

careful   + ly = _____         angry     + ly = _____

unsteady  + ly = _____         sudden    + ly = _____

<u>**Now use the words you have made to complete the sentences below.**</u>

1   The man shouted _____ at the boys who were trespassing in his garden.

2   The team played very _____ and won the match 3-0.

3   The boy was told off for speaking _____ to his teacher.

4   After the heavy shower of rain, the sun _____ came out.

5   The policeman asked the motorist _____ for his licence.

6   The hungry dogs ate their dinner _____.

7   We at last arrived home _____ after the long journey.

8   The drunk man walked _____.

9   She _____ placed the glass vase on the top shelf.

10  The boy _____ refused to share his sweets.

# Adding ly to base words with suffixes

Suffix ly can be added to base words which
already have a suffix.

e.g.    tact<u>ful</u> + ly = tact<u>fully</u>.

content<u>ed</u> + ly = content<u>edly</u>.

**Do the word-sums below to make ADVERBS ending in ly .**

**Follow the suffixing rules you have learnt when adding BOTH suffixes.**

e.g. bit~~e~~ + ing + ly = bitingly    (DROP 'e' and JUST ADD)

hope      +    ful + ly = _____        noise   + less + ly = _____

repeat   +    ed + ly = _____          play      +    ful + ly = _____

faith      +    ful + ly = _____         drunk   +    en + ly = _____

care       + less + ly = _____         decide +    ed + ly = _____

excite    +    ed + ly = _____          fool       +    ish + ly = _____

thank    +    ful + ly = _____          love      +    ing + ly = _____

amaze   +    ing + ly = _____         strike    +    ing + ly = _____

cheer    +    ful + ly = _____          taste    +    ful + ly = _____

devote   +    ed + ly = _____          beauty +    ful + ly = _____

madden +    ing + ly = _____          joke      +    ing + ly = _____

**Now choose 5 of the above words you have made and use them in
sentences of your own on the lines below.**

_____

_____

_____

_____

_____

_____

_____

_____

# Suffix en

The suffix **en** is a <u>VERB</u> suffix. It changes an
<u>ADJECTIVE</u> into a <u>VERB</u> meaning 'to make' or 'to become'.

e.g.    black + en = black<u>en</u> (to make black).

sick + en = sick<u>en</u>   (to become sick).

## Add the en suffix to the words below.

short      + en = _____ to make shorter

thick      + en = _____ to make thicker

deep      + en = _____ to make deeper

dark      + en = _____ to make dark

weak      + en = _____ to become weak

deaf      + en = _____ to make deaf

tight      + en = _____ to make tight

soft      + en = _____ to make soft

light      + en = _____ to make light

damp      + en = _____ to make damp

slack      + en = _____ to make loose

hard      + en = _____ to make hard

length    + en = _____ to make longer

strength + en = _____ to make stronger

**<u>In the list above there are five pairs of opposites.</u>**
**<u>Write them in the boxes below.</u>**

*(The first one has been done for you as an example.)*

| **soften – harden** | | |
| --- | --- | --- |

| | |
| --- | --- |

# Suffix

**In the word-square below find the 12 words to which you
can add suffix en .Write each word in the list beside the square.**

*(Words go ACROSS and DOWN only.)*

| j | o | w | f | a | d | a | m | p | u |
|---|---|---|---|---|---|---|---|---|---|
| s | h | a | r | p | r | s | o | f | t |
| h | y | t | i | c | o | l | v | i | f |
| o | m | a | g | f | s | w | e | e | t |
| r | t | q | h | i | u | z | b | n | x |
| t | i | a | t | h | i | c | k | j | k |
| v | g | w | e | a | k | g | n | g | s |
| b | h | e | h | a | r | d | y | m | v |
| d | t | r | o | l | e | n | g | t | h |
| l | s | d | a | r | k | c | h | x | p |

d _ _ _
d _ _ _
f _ _ _ _ _
h _ _ _
l _ _ _ _
s _ _ _ _
s _ _ _ _
s _ _ _
s _ _ _ _
t _ _ _ _
t _ _ _ _
w _ _ _

**Now add suffix en to each of the words you have found and use
each one to complete the sentences below.**

1   Can you please _____ this screw because it has become loose.

2   You must _____ a stamp to make it stick.

3   Your pencil is blunt, so please _____ it.

4   You add sugar to _____ things.

5   The skirt was too long so I decided to _____ it.

6   She added some flour to _____ the soup.

7   Liquid cement soon begins to _____ after mixing.

8   Some people use blinds or shutters to _____ their bedroom so
    that no light can get in.

9   The boy liked to _____ his little sister by putting a plastic spider
    in her bed!

10  In spring the days begin to _____ giving us more hours of
    daylight.

11  The tiny puppy began to _____ as it would not drink any milk.

12  Butter begins to _____ if you take it out of the fridge.

# Suffix ish

The suffix ish is an **ADJECTIVE** ending. It can have different meanings:

boyish = like a boy.

greyish = a little bit grey.

Scottish = nationality.

The suffix ish begins with a **VOWEL**, so you might have to follow the **DOUBLE** or **DROP 'e'** suffixing rules.

e.g.      red + ish = reddish (DOUBLE).

white + ish = whitish (DROP 'e').

### Add suffix ish to the base words below.
### Follow the correct suffixing rule: DOUBLE, DROP 'e' or JUST ADD.

white + ish = _____          fat     + ish = _____

green + ish = _____          cool   + ish = _____

steep + ish = _____          style  + ish = _____

snob  + ish = _____          girl    + ish = _____

tickle + ish = _____          slug   + ish = _____

wet    + ish = _____          round + ish = _____

### Unscramble the words below to find nationalities ending in suffix ish .

### e.g. S N L E I G H = English

1 HAINSD    = _____          6 HSWIEDS = _____

2 HITRUKS = _____          7 HIEJWS    = _____

3 HINFINS  = _____          8 NPAIHSS = _____

4 OSPLIH    = _____          9 ISHRI       = _____

5 SHTRIBI  = _____          10 IEFMSLH = _____

# Suffix ish

**Find a base word hidden in each line of letters to which you can add suffix ish to complete the sentences below.**

Example

o l e n d u k (p i n k) c h a b    _____pink_____

At sunset the clouds had a **pinkish** tinge.

1   t a x j e p l u m p o n g f u   _____

She was very pretty despite being a little _____.

2   s h e e p a b p i v c h i l l   _____

The boy felt very _____ after being caught cheating.

3   s a p e c k d i l h a n g o c   _____

Snacks are useful between meals if you are _____.

4   j a m w e n t b a d a m p e l   _____

Because the roof leaked, the house felt _____.

5   x p d s e l f a q h a r m g o   _____

He was unpopular because of his _____ behaviour.

6   j u p s i c k e g f o o l h e   _____

It is extremely _____ to drink and drive.

7   m i l d o d u s k g c h i l d   _____

The girl was very _____ for her age.

8   o w i m p g o m e l t u f t g   _____

The boy had an _____ grin on his face.

9   g i p r a o e v f e v e r b y   _____

When you have the flu, you often feel _____.

10   w b o i l b o o r u d n o r t   _____

A _____ person is coarse and ill-mannered.

11   a b l o n d i m p a r e s t i   _____

The woman had _____ hair which had obviously been dyed.

12   r w a r m u g r o l f r e t o   _____

As it was a _____ day, we decided to have lunch outside.

# Suffix er : (more)

The suffix er is added to **ADJECTIVES** to mean 'more'.
e.g.    tall + er = tall**er** ('more' tall).

As er is a **VOWEL** suffix, you may have to
**DOUBLE** or **DROP 'e'** when adding it to base words.

e.g.    făt + er = fatter (DOUBLE).
wide + ĕr = wider (DROP 'e').

### Add suffix er to the ADJECTIVES below.
### Follow the correct rule: DOUBLE, DROP 'e' or JUST ADD.

deep + er = _____        cheap + er = _____

safe + er = _____        fresh + er = _____

tight + er = _____        slim + er = _____

big + er = _____        clever + er = _____

hot + er = _____        hard + er = _____

fit + er = _____        late + er = _____

### Now use the words you have made to complete the sentences below.

1   He felt _____ after his shower.

2   She was a lot _____ after her diet.

3   Deepa is _____ than her sister and is top of her class.

4   Driving a car is _____ than riding a motorbike.

5   His trousers felt _____ after eating Christmas dinner.

6   A horse is _____ than a donkey.

7   In a sale you get things _____ than normal.

8   He always arrived at work _____ than everybody else.

9   He felt a lot _____ once he took up jogging.

10  The river was _____ than usual because of the heavy rain.

11  It is much _____ in the south of Spain than in England.

12  The mattress was _____ than the one on her own bed.

# Suffix er (agent)

The suffix er is added to the end of base words to show
a person or thing that does something.

e.g.     boxer = someone who boxes.
blender = a machine which blends.

The er suffix in these words shows agency.

Write down 6 machines or gadgets which end in er .
Think of things which are used in the house or garden.

_____          _____          _____

_____          _____          _____

Now write down 6 people who do jobs or activities.
The ones you choose must end in er .

_____          _____          _____

_____          _____          _____

Follow the suffixing rules you have learnt when adding er to
base words. In the exercise below you will have to DOUBLE,
DROP 'e' or JUST ADD.

jog   + er = _____          write  + er = _____

ride  + er = _____          lead   + er = _____

paint + er = _____          weave + er = _____

ward + er = _____          dance + er = _____

rob   + er = _____          train  + er = _____

shop + er = _____          swim  + er = _____

vote + er = _____          dream + er = _____

play  + er = _____          smoke + er = _____

# Suffix er (agent)

**Find 15 words in the word-square below which end in suffix er .**

**Match each word to the clues below.**

*(Words go ACROSS and DOWN only.)*

| s | i | n | g | e | r | l | a | m | d |
|---|---|---|---|---|---|---|---|---|---|
| j | o | g | g | e | r | t | b | q | o |
| k | w | a | i | t | e | r | o | s | c |
| f | a | r | m | e | r | a | x | n | l |
| c | f | d | t | c | h | d | e | r | i |
| a | t | e | a | c | h | e | r | o | m |
| m | i | n | e | r | u | r | a | b | b |
| p | b | e | d | i | v | e | r | b | e |
| e | g | r | e | p | o | r | t | e | r |
| r | i | j | s | k | a | t | e | r | v |

This person plants crops and keeps animals  _ _ _ _ _ _

This person must be careful he or she doesn't fall  _ _ _ _ _ _ _ _

This person might help you with this exercise!  _ _ _ _ _ _ _ _

This person keeps very fit  _ _ _ _ _ _

This person sleeps in a tent  _ _ _ _ _ _

This person needs a good voice  _ _ _ _ _ _

This person is always looking for a good story  _ _ _ _ _ _ _ _

This person needs to be good at business  _ _ _ _ _ _

This person can move quickly on ice  _ _ _ _ _ _

This person works underground  _ _ _ _ _

This person might have to weed the flower beds  _ _ _ _ _ _ _ _ _

This person spends time underwater  _ _ _ _ _

This person serves you in a restaurant  _ _ _ _ _ _

This person fights in a ring  _ _ _ _ _

This person steals from banks  _ _ _ _ _ _

# Adding er to base words ending in 'y'

## Rule

When we add suffix er to a base word ending
in 'y', we must CHANGE 'y' to 'i'.

e.g. lazy + er = lazier.

**Add suffix er to the base words below which all end in 'y'.**

crazy + er = _____     heavy + er = _____

empty + er = _____     noisy + er = _____

pretty + er = _____     messy + er = _____

dirty + er = _____     silly + er = _____

dry + er = _____     easy + er = _____

happy + er = _____     juicy + er = _____

**Now use ALL your suffixing rules to do the word-sums below. Choose
the correct rule: DOUBLE, DROP 'e', CHANGE 'y' to 'i' or JUST ADD.**

| e.g. | BASE WORD | | | RULE? | | RESULT |
|---|---|---|---|---|---|---|
| | wide | + | er | Drop 'e' | = | wider |

| BASE WORD | SUFFIX | | RULE? | RESULT |
|---|---|---|---|---|
| steep | + | er | _____ | _____ |
| white | + | er | _____ | _____ |
| tasty | + | er | _____ | _____ |
| healthy | + | er | _____ | _____ |
| clever | + | er | _____ | _____ |
| wet | + | er | _____ | _____ |
| dear | + | er | _____ | _____ |
| tidy | + | er | _____ | _____ |
| shallow | + | er | _____ | _____ |
| red | + | er | _____ | _____ |
| greedy | + | er | _____ | _____ |
| brave | + | er | _____ | _____ |

# Suffix er : Revision

**Suffix er can have 2 meanings: What are they?**

1   It can mean _____

2   It can mean _____

**Put the words with er suffix into the right box.**

| | | MORE | AGENT |
|---|---|---|---|
| wiser | greener | _____ | _____ |
| drummer | murderer | _____ | _____ |
| shaver | sooner | _____ | _____ |
| robber | owner | _____ | _____ |
| ruder | cheaper | _____ | _____ |
| thinner | runner | _____ | _____ |
| later | skater | _____ | _____ |
| madder | redder | _____ | _____ |
| ruler | dreamer | _____ | _____ |

**Now put each word into the right box according to the suffixing rule which has been followed. Look at the example which has been done for you.** *(There should be 6 in each box.)*

| JUST ADD | DOUBLE | DROP 'e' |
|---|---|---|
| | | shaver = shavé+er |
| _____ | _____ | _____ |
| _____ | _____ | _____ |
| _____ | _____ | _____ |
| _____ | _____ | _____ |
| _____ | _____ | _____ |

# Suffix est

The suffix **est** is used to mean 'the most' when making comparisons. It is added to **ADJECTIVES**.

e.g. Mount Everest is the high<u>est</u> mountain in the world.

The suffix **est** is a **VOWEL** suffix, so remember to follow the **DOUBLE** or **DROP 'e'** rule when necessary.

e.g. big + est = bi<u>gg</u>est.

fin<u>e</u> + est = finest.

If the base word ends in 'y', **CHANGE 'y' to 'i'** when you add the suffix.

e.g. happ<u>y</u> + est = happ<u>i</u>est.

**Add suffixes er and est to the ADJECTIVES below.**
**Follow the correct suffixing rule. Look at the example given.**

| ADJECTIVE | ADJECTIVE + 'er' | ADJECTIVE + 'est' |
|---|---|---|
| e.g. long | long<u>er</u> | long<u>est</u> |
| flat | | |
| lazy | | |
| wide | | |
| deep | | |
| hot | | |
| cheap | | |
| slim | | |
| cool | | |
| thin | | |
| dry | | |

# Suffixes er and est

**Choose suffix er or est to complete the words in the sentences below.**

1 David is tall___ than most boys of his age, but he is not the tall___ in his class.

2 The object of the game is to make few___ mistakes than other players, and the one with the few___ mistakes is the winner.

3 The sun is bright___ than the moon and is the bright___ object in the sky.

4 This winter has been the cold___ I remember and certainly a lot cold___ than last year.

5 It was the soft___ mattress I had ever slept on and, as a result, I had a much deep___ sleep than normal.

6 The short___ day is in December and after this time the days begin to get long___.

7 Staying in "B&Bs" is cheap___ than in hotels, but the cheap___ holiday of all is camping.

8 The thick___ book I ever read had 900 pages and it took me far long___ to read than I had expected!

9 My grandmother was the kind___ person I have ever known but my grandfather was one of the mean___.

10 Trains are usually fast___ than cars, but the quick___ way to travel is by air.

## QUIZ

**Test your general knowledge by answering the questions below.**

1 What is the highest mountain in Great Britain? _____

2 What is the deepest lake in Great Britain? _____

3 What is the oldest university in Great Britain? _____

4 Who is the richest woman in Great Britain? _____

5 What is the largest mammal in the world? _____

6 What is the longest river in the world? _____

7 What is the smallest planet? _____

8 Which is the biggest continent? _____

# Suffix Revision Sheet

### Look at the suffixes in the box below.

| ful | less | ness | ly | y | ish | en |
|-----|------|------|----|----|-----|-----|

Which suffix is a <u>NOUN</u> suffix?      _____

Which 4 suffixes are <u>ADJECTIVE</u> suffixes?      _____    _____

     _____    _____

Which is the <u>ADVERB</u> suffix?      _____

Which is a <u>VERB</u> suffix?      _____

### Look at the base words below. What suffix(es) can be added to each one? The first one has been done for you as an example.

1  care  ( ____**ful, less**____ )      7  deep  ( _____ )

2  smart ( _____ )      8  rude  ( _____ )

3  shy  ( _____ )      9  thank ( _____ )

4  damp ( _____ )      10  storm ( _____ )

5  light  ( _____ )      11  itch  ( _____ )

6  fear  ( _____ )      12  slow  ( _____ )

### The suffix combinations below can be added to base words.

| _____ishness | _____fully | _____lessly |
|--------------|------------|-------------|
| _____ened | _____lessness | |

### Now use one of the combinations above to add to each base word.

1  power_____     5  short_____     9  sleep_____

2  wrong_____     6  job_____     10  fool_____

3  child_____     7  colour_____     11  threat_____

4  self_____     8  straight_____     12  tight_____

# Suffix Revision Sheet

**There is one missing suffix in each of the sentences below.**
**Find the missing suffix by choosing from the box below.**

| ed | ish | less | ful | ness | ly |
|----|-----|------|-----|------|----|
| | es | ing | en | y | |

1   The   self   boy   did   not   have   many   friends   .

2   She   decided   to   short   her   dress   .

3   The   rest   child   kept   moving   around   the   room   .

4   After   mend   his   bike   he   washed   his   hands   .

5   We   could   see   by   the   bright   of   the   moon   .

6   The   children   walked   along   the   sand   beach   .

7   The   oranges   were   stacked   in   box   .

8   The   tear   child   stopped   crying   when   his   mother   picked   him   up   .

9   The   children   were   told   to   work   silent   .

10   The   police   suspect   that   the   man   was   a   drug   dealer   .

**Choose 2 suffixes from the box below to complete the words**
**in the sentences.**

| ful | en | ly | less | ed | ness | ish |
|-----|----|----|------|----|------|-----|

1   They were fright_____ to discover someone lurking in the garden.

2   In the end, the dispute was settled peace_____.

3   She was not liked because of her self_____.

4   The chef thick_____ the soup with some flour.

5   He always lost marks in exams because of care_____.

6   The ballerina danced so grace_____ that the audience was spellbound.

7   She fool_____ locked herself out of her house.

8   He sharp_____ his pencil before doing the exercise.

# Suffix Revision Sheet

## Write the BASE word for each of the words below.

1 sobbing _____

2 starry _____

3 frighten _____

4 fleecy _____

5 smoky _____

6 spotty _____

7 trimmed _____

8 feverish _____

9 wiry _____

10 freezing _____

11 friendless _____

12 widen _____

## Do the word-sums below.
## Follow the correct rule: DOUBLE, DROP 'e' or JUST ADD.

1 stride + ing = _____

2 tickle + ish = _____

3 fur + y = _____

4 soap + y = _____

5 feed + ing = _____

6 grub + y = _____

7 flake + y = _____

8 graze + ing = _____

9 lout + ish = _____

10 stain + ed = _____

11 breeze + y = _____

12 bag + y = _____

## Choose the correct suffix from the box below to add
## to each base word.

| es | ful | less | ness | y | en | er | ly |
|----|-----|------|------|---|----|----|----|

1 end + _____ = _____

2 ditch + _____ = _____

3 silent + _____ = _____

4 foolish + _____ = _____

5 gloom + _____ = _____

6 peace + _____ = _____

7 threat + _____ = _____

8 climb + _____ = _____

# Suffix Revision Sheet

### Write the BASE word for each of the words below.

1 gripped _____ 7 cheerfully _____

2 snobbish _____ 8 homelessness _____

3 exciting _____ 9 tasty _____

4 icy _____ 10 suddenness _____

5 hardened _____ 11 spiky _____

6 drummer _____ 12 squatter _____

### Do the word-sums below.
### Follow the correct rule: DOUBLE, DROP 'e' or JUST ADD.

1 creep + y = _____ 7 shine + y = _____

2 waste + ful = _____ 8 steam + y = _____

3 loose + en + ed = _____ 9 fool + ish + ly = _____

4 slop + y = _____ 10 jut + ed = _____

5 stun + ed = _____ 11 deaf + en + ing = _____

6 sin + ful = _____ 12 trap + er = _____

### Choose the correct suffix from the box below to add
### to each base word.

| es | ful | less | ness | y | en | er | ly |
|----|-----|------|------|---|----|----|----|

1 snow + _____ = _____

2 job + _____ = _____

3 excited + _____ = _____

4 spite + _____ = _____

5 tired + _____ = _____

6 gold + _____ = _____

7 work + _____ = _____

8 suffix + _____ = _____

# Suffix Revision Sheet

## Write the BASE word for each of the words below.

1 ticklish _____

2 pitifully _____

3 emptiness _____

4 noiselessly _____

5 inviting _____

6 wobbly _____

7 loosened _____

8 surviving _____

9 jokingly _____

10 tugged _____

11 noisily _____

12 bossiness _____

## Do the word-sums below. Follow the correct rule: DOUBLE, DROP 'e', CHANGE 'y' to 'i' or JUST ADD.

1 mean + ness = _____

2 knit + ed = _____

3 policy + es = _____

4 destroy + ed = _____

5 terrify + ing = _____

6 flab + y = _____

7 taste + y = _____

8 sweet + en = _____

9 throb + ing = _____

10 notify + ed = _____

11 happy + est = _____

12 Dane + ish = _____

## Choose the correct suffix from the box below to add to each base word.

| es | ful | ish | ness | y | en | er | ly |
|---|---|---|---|---|---|---|---|

1 employ + _____ = _____

2 tax + _____ = _____

3 cheek + _____ = _____

4 child + _____ = _____

5 respect + _____ = _____

6 wood + _____ = _____

7 extreme + _____ = _____

8 homesick + _____ = _____

# Suffix Revision: DOUBLING v̆c|v

**Circle the 12 word-sums below which require the DOUBLING rule.**
**Look for the VC|V pattern.**

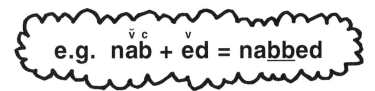

e.g. nab + ed = na**bb**ed

**Remember that** $\boxed{y}$ **is a VOWEL suffix.**

| | | |
|---|---|---|
| sleep + ing | slip + ed | pat + ed |
| rain + ing | walk + ed | nut + y |
| eat + ing | drip + ing | care + ful |
| creep + y | dig + ing | cut + ing |
| waste + ful | sun + y | play + ful |
| red + en | milk + y | rob + er |
| slide + ing | mend + ed | see + ing |
| rest + ful | creak + ing | jot + ed |
| fade + ed | wet + er | joke + ing |
| float + ed | hum + ing | stay + ed |

**Now write out the completed words on the lines below.**

1 _____      5 _____      9 _____

2 _____      6 _____      10 _____

3 _____      7 _____      11 _____

4 _____      8 _____      12 _____

# Suffix Revision: DOUBLE or JUST ADD

## Choose the correct rule to add to the base words below.
### Remember that  y  is a VOWEL suffix.

**TEST ONE**                         **TEST TWO**

1  beat  +    en = _____         1  deaf  + en = _____

2  fret  +    ing = _____        2  dig   + er = _____

3  swim  +    er = _____         3  dip   + ed = _____

4  shoot +    ing = _____        4  heal  + er = _____

5  kid   +    ing = _____        5  deep  + est = _____

6  slop  +    y = _____          6  flab  + y = _____

7  feel  +    ing = _____        7  yap   + ing = _____

8  pot   +    er = _____         8  chop  + y = _____

9  red   + ness = _____          9  groan + ing = _____

10 club  +    ed = _____         10 big   + ish = _____

11 wet   +    ish = _____        11 grin  + ed = _____

12 seep  +    ing = _____        12 chop  + er = _____

13 flip  +    ed = _____         13 room  + y = _____

14 bag   +    y = _____          14 whip  + ed = _____

15 grain +    y = _____          15 fit   + ful = _____

              **Score** _____              **Score** _____
                   **15**                          **15**

# Suffix Revision: DROP 'e'

**Circle the 12 word-sums below which require the DROP 'e' rule.**
**Remember that** $\boxed{\textbf{y}}$ **is a VOWEL suffix.**

| | | |
|---|---|---|
| late + ness | wobble + y | hate + ful |
| wheeze + ing | amaze + ment | awake + en |
| purple + ish | excite + ment | spike + y |
| polite + ly | surprise + ing | bottle + ful |
| hope + ful | invade + er | complete + ly |
| achieve + ment | price + y | agree + ment |
| change + less | judge + ing | fine + ly |
| drizzle + y | require + ment | like + ness |
| extreme + ly | time + less | graze + ing |
| complete + ness | wide + ly | style + ish |

**Now write out the completed words on the lines below.**

1 _____     5 _____     9 _____

2 _____     6 _____     10 _____

3 _____     7 _____     11 _____

4 _____     8 _____     12 _____

# Suffix Revision: DROP 'e' or JUST ADD

**Choose the correct rule to add to the base words below.**

**Remember that** $\boxed{\text{y}}$ **is a VOWEL suffix.**

**TEST ONE**

1   brave      +      ly = _____

2   tingle     +      y = _____

3   wise       +      ly = _____

4   coarse     + ness = _____

5   consume +      er = _____

6   shape      + less = _____

7   gape       +      ing = _____

8   tune       +      ful = _____

9   ripe       +      en = _____

10  haze       +      y = _____

11  fade       +      ing = _____

12  white      +      er = _____

13  live       +      ly = _____

14  forgive    + ness = _____

15  price      +      y = _____

**Score** _____

**15**

**TEST TWO**

1   shame      +      ful = _____

2   noble      + ness = _____

3   stripe     +      y = _____

4   huge       +      ly = _____

5   sponge     +      y = _____

6   weave      +      er = _____

7   inflate    +      ing = _____

8   close      + ness = _____

9   bubble     +      y = _____

10  active     +      ly = _____

11  quake      +      ing = _____

12  revenge +      ful = _____

13  smuggle +      er = _____

14  shape      +      ly = _____

15  operate +      ing = _____

**Score** _____

**15**

# Suffix Revision: CHANGE 'y' to 'i'

**Look at the word-sums below. All the base words end in 'y'.**
**If you need to CHANGE 'y' to 'i', circle with a RED pen.**
**If you JUST ADD the suffix, circle with a BLUE pen.**

| | | |
|---|---|---|
| baby + ish | fortify + ed | sway + ed |
| happy + er | enjoy + ment | pretty + ly |
| mercy + ful | annoy + ing | army + es |
| empty + ed | tasty + est | supply + ing |
| array + ed | spray + ed | hungry + ly |
| dirty + est | pity + less | destroy + er |
| hurry + ing | employ + ment | |

**Now write the complete word in the correct list below.**

| CHANGE 'y' to 'i' | JUST ADD |
|---|---|
| _____ | _____ |
| _____ | _____ |
| _____ | _____ |
| _____ | _____ |
| _____ | _____ |
| _____ | _____ |
| _____ | _____ |
| _____ | _____ |

# Suffix Revision: CHANGE 'y' to 'i'

**Change the verbs below to the PAST tense by adding the suffix** `ed` .
**Follow the correct rule: CHANGE 'y' to 'i' or JUST ADD.**

| PAST TENSE | | PAST TENSE | |
|---|---|---|---|
| annoy | _____ | betray | _____ |
| survey | _____ | bully | _____ |
| defy | _____ | annoy | _____ |
| reply | _____ | obey | _____ |
| sway | _____ | identify | _____ |
| multiply | _____ | portray | _____ |
| curtsey | _____ | study | _____ |
| pray | _____ | satisfy | _____ |
| apply | _____ | convey | _____ |
| tidy | _____ | stray | _____ |

**Make the following words PLURAL. Follow the correct rule:**
**CHANGE 'y' to 'i' and add suffix** `es` **or JUST ADD the suffix** `s` .

| PLURAL | | PLURAL | |
|---|---|---|---|
| valley | _____ | journey | _____ |
| baby | _____ | policy | _____ |
| jockey | _____ | display | _____ |
| currency | _____ | tray | _____ |
| trolley | _____ | vacancy | _____ |
| toy | _____ | joy | _____ |
| jelly | _____ | comedy | _____ |
| kidney | _____ | abbey | _____ |
| butterfly | _____ | enemy | _____ |
| buoy | _____ | turkey | _____ |

# Rule Revision Sheet

**What is the BASE word in the words below which all have suffixes?**
**What rule had been followed to add the suffix to the base word?**

DOUBLE?    DROP 'e'?    CHANGE 'y' to 'i'?    JUST ADD?

|  | WORD | SUFFIX | RULE | BASE WORD |
|---|---|---|---|---|
| e.g. | snobbish | ish | DOUBLE | snob |

| WORD | SUFFIX | RULE | BASE WORD |
|---|---|---|---|
| winner | | | |
| pitiful | | | |
| skidded | | | |
| shady | | | |
| shiny | | | |
| typing | | | |
| employer | | | |
| studied | | | |
| steeply | | | |
| stylish | | | |
| tidiness | | | |
| cheating | | | |
| greenish | | | |
| ponies | | | |
| flatten | | | |
| chatty | | | |
| slaving | | | |
| wetter | | | |
| hobbies | | | |
| smoothness | | | |

# Rule Revision Sheet

**What is the BASE word in the words below which all have suffixes?**
**What rule had been followed to add the suffix to the base word?**

{ DOUBLE? }　{ DROP 'e'? }　{ CHANGE 'y' to 'i'? }　{ JUST ADD? }

|  | WORD | SUFFIX | RULE | BASE WORD |
|---|---|---|---|---|
| e.g. | snobbish | ish | DOUBLE | snob |

| WORD | SUFFIX | RULE | BASE WORD |
|---|---|---|---|
| bubbly | _____ | _____ | _____ |
| nutty | _____ | _____ | _____ |
| preparing | _____ | _____ | _____ |
| skipping | _____ | _____ | _____ |
| smallish | _____ | _____ | _____ |
| busiest | _____ | _____ | _____ |
| successful | _____ | _____ | _____ |
| shopper | _____ | _____ | _____ |
| prickly | _____ | _____ | _____ |
| pastries | _____ | _____ | _____ |
| Danish | _____ | _____ | _____ |
| terrified | _____ | _____ | _____ |
| trapped | _____ | _____ | _____ |
| steepness | _____ | _____ | _____ |
| happier | _____ | _____ | _____ |
| smarten | _____ | _____ | _____ |
| foggy | _____ | _____ | _____ |
| dozing | _____ | _____ | _____ |
| penalties | _____ | _____ | _____ |
| murderer | _____ | _____ | _____ |

# Rule Revision Sheet

<u>**What is the BASE word in the words below which all have suffixes?**</u>
<u>**What rule had been followed to add the suffix to the base word?**</u>

{ **DOUBLE?** }  { **DROP 'e'?** }  { **CHANGE 'y' to 'i'?** }  { **JUST ADD?** }

| | WORD | SUFFIX | RULE | BASE WORD |
|---|---|---|---|---|
| e.g. | snobbish | ish | DOUBLE | snob |

| WORD | SUFFIX | RULE | BASE WORD |
|---|---|---|---|
| strummed | | | |
| Polish | | | |
| boastful | | | |
| gladden | | | |
| dignified | | | |
| gypsies | | | |
| freezer | | | |
| plunging | | | |
| foolish | | | |
| clumsiest | | | |
| wheeled | | | |
| freely | | | |
| wakeful | | | |
| wallabies | | | |
| dubbed | | | |
| gravely | | | |
| groomed | | | |
| sagging | | | |
| tasty | | | |
| commuter | | | |

# Rule Practice Sheet

 **DOUBLE?**  **DROP 'e'?**   **JUST ADD?**

## Choose the correct rule to add the suffixes to the base words below.

| **TEST ONE** | **TEST TWO** |
|---|---|
| 1   oil        +        y = _____ | 1   heap     +   ed = _____ |
| 2   wit        +        y = _____ | 2   clip      +   ed = _____ |
| 3   white    + ness = _____ | 3   bounce +       y = _____ |
| 4   sneeze +   ing = _____ | 4   snore    +  ing = _____ |
| 5   mad      +    en = _____ | 5   ban       +   ed = _____ |
| 6   guide    +   ing = _____ | 6   slave     +  ish = _____ |
| 7   nail       +    ed = _____ | 7   mood    +       y = _____ |
| 8   slug      +   ish = _____ | 8   span     +  ing = _____ |
| 9   peel      +   ing = _____ | 9   spine    + less = _____ |
| 10  poke    +   ing = _____ | 10  cloud   +       y = _____ |
| 11  cheese +       y = _____ | 11  skin     +   ed = _____ |
| 12  load    +    ed = _____ | 12  escape +  ing = _____ |
| 13  brag    +   ing = _____ | 13  trail    +   ed = _____ |
| 14  prickle +       y = _____ | 14  spot    +       y = _____ |
| 15  tin       +    ed = _____ | 15  flame   +  ing = _____ |

**Score** _____         **Score** _____

15         15

# Rule Practice Sheet

 DOUBLE?  DROP 'e'? JUST ADD?

## Choose the correct rule to add the suffixes to the base words below.

**TEST ONE**

1  deep  + est = _____
2  smoke  +  y = _____
3  red  + en = _____
4  care  + ful = _____
5  slum  +  y = _____
6  propose + ing = _____
7  sag  + ing = _____
8  sip  + ed = _____
9  time  + less = _____
10  glare  + ing = _____
11  yellow  + ish = _____
12  log  + ing = _____
13  ripe  + est = _____
14  sheep  + ish = _____
15  brave  + er = _____

**TEST TWO**

1  rose  +  y = _____
2  brain  +  y = _____
3  jut  + ed = _____
4  divide  + ing = _____
5  tin  +  y = _____
6  wide  + en = _____
7  dope  +  y = _____
8  hope  + ful = _____
9  whet  + ing = _____
10  slim  + er = _____
11  cheap  + est = _____
12  freckle +  y = _____
13  steam  + ing = _____
14  hoot  + ed = _____
15  fit  + ing = _____

Score _____   15

Score _____   15

# Rule Practice Sheet

DOUBLE?    DROP 'e'?    CHANGE 'y' to 'i'?    JUST ADD?

## Use the correct rule to add the suffixes to the base words below.

| BASE WORD | SUFFIX | RULE | RESULT |
|---|---|---|---|
| play | er | | |
| wit | y | | |
| gaze | ing | | |
| penny | less | | |
| web | ed | | |
| slime | y | | |
| rosy | er | | |
| spite | ful | | |
| cry | ed | | |
| fry | ing | | |
| prickle | y | | |
| silly | ness | | |
| slim | ing | | |
| stare | ing | | |
| skid | ing | | |
| lazy | ly | | |
| waste | ing | | |
| waste | ful | | |
| late | ly | | |
| sin | er | | |

# Rule Practice Sheet

{ DOUBLE? }   { DROP 'e'? }   { CHANGE 'y' to 'i'? }   { JUST ADD? }

## Use the correct rule to add the suffixes to the base words below.

| BASE WORD | SUFFIX | RULE | RESULT |
|-----------|--------|------|--------|
| lonely | er | | |
| snap | y | | |
| seed | y | | |
| glide | er | | |
| nag | ed | | |
| steady | ly | | |
| craze | y | | |
| flop | y | | |
| pretty | er | | |
| shout | ing | | |
| sin | ful | | |
| dusty | est | | |
| clap | ing | | |
| shine | y | | |
| crazy | ly | | |
| steep | est | | |
| shake | ing | | |
| wide | en | | |
| pad | ing | | |
| dismay | ed | | |

# Rule Practice Sheet

{ DOUBLE? }   { DROP 'e'? }   { CHANGE 'y' to 'i'? }   { JUST ADD? }

**Use the correct rule to add the suffixes to the base words below.**

| BASE WORD | SUFFIX | RULE | RESULT |
|---|---|---|---|
| excite | ing | | |
| grab | ed | | |
| bone | y | | |
| empty | ed | | |
| thirsty | est | | |
| smog | y | | |
| blaze | ing | | |
| employ | er | | |
| clumsy | er | | |
| hate | ful | | |
| grime | y | | |
| split | ing | | |
| steep | er | | |
| simplify | ed | | |
| peel | ed | | |
| waste | ful | | |
| slam | ed | | |
| charity | es | | |
| argue | ing | | |
| grin | ed | | |

# Rule Practice Sheet

  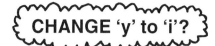 

DOUBLE?  DROP 'e'?  CHANGE 'y' to 'i'?  JUST ADD?

**Use the correct rule to add the suffixes to the base words below.**

| BASE WORD | SUFFIX | RULE | RESULT |
|---|---|---|---|
| | | | |
| | | | |
| | | | |
| | | | |
| | | | |
| | | | |
| | | | |
| | | | |
| | | | |
| | | | |
| | | | |
| | | | |
| | | | |
| | | | |
| | | | |
| | | | |
| | | | |
| | | | |

# APPENDICES

## Appendix 1        DOUBLE Rule

The words below all have the V̆C pattern and can take either suffix 'ing' or 'ed', or both suffixes.

| | | | | | | |
|---|---|---|---|---|---|---|
| bag | dig | hem | net | set | spin | top |
| ban | dip | hit | nip | sham | spit | tot |
| bat | drag | hog | nod | shin | split | trap |
| beg | drip | hop | pad | ship | stab | trim |
| bet | drop | hug | pat | shop | stem | trip |
| bid | drug | hum | peg | shred | step | trot |
| blot | drum | jab | pet | shrug | stop | tug |
| bob | dub | jam | pin | shun | stub | vet |
| brag | fan | jig | plan | shut | stun | wag |
| bud | fit | jog | plod | sin | strap | web |
| can | flap | jot | plop | sip | strip | wed |
| cap | flip | jut | plot | sit | strut | wet |
| chat | flit | kid | plug | skid | sun | whet |
| chop | flog | knit | put | skin | swap | whip |
| chug | flop | lag | quit | skip | swat | win |
| clap | fret | let | ram | slam | swig | yap |
| clip | gag | log | rap | slap | tag | zip |
| clog | get | lug | rid | slim | tan | |
| clot | grab | man | rig | slip | tap | |
| club | grin | map | rip | slot | thin | |
| con | grip | mob | rob | snap | throb | |
| cram | grit | mop | rub | snip | thud | |
| cut | gum | mug | run | sob | tin | |
| dab | gut | nap | sag | span | tip | |

# Appendix 2     DROP 'e' Rule

The words below are all verbs which end in 'e', and can take either the 'ing' or the 'ed' suffix, or both suffixes. The list concentrates on base words where the final 'e' lengthens the vowel (magic 'e' pattern), but some other patterns have been included as well.

| | | | | | | |
|---|---|---|---|---|---|---|
| accuse | continue | excite | ignite | pace | restore | stroke |
| admire | convince | expire | improve | paste | retire | struggle |
| adore | cope | explore | include | pave | revise | surprise |
| advise | crackle | face | inflate | perspire | ride | survive |
| amaze | crave | fade | inhale | pervade | ripple | swerve |
| amble | create | feature | inspire | phone | rise | swipe |
| amuse | crumble | fiddle | invade | pile | rope | take |
| argue | cuddle | file | invite | pine | rule | tape |
| baffle | cure | fine | issue | pipe | salute | taste |
| bake | cycle | fire | joke | place | save | tickle |
| battle | dabble | flame | jostle | plunge | scare | time |
| behave | dance | freeze | judge | pollute | scrabble | topple |
| bite | dangle | fumble | juggle | postpone | scuffle | trade |
| blare | dare | gamble | lace | praise | seize | tremble |
| blaze | date | gape | laze | prance | serve | trouble |
| bounce | daze | gaze | leave | prepare | settle | trudge |
| brake | dazzle | giggle | like | price | shade | tumble |
| bundle | debate | give | line | prickle | shake | type |
| burgle | delete | glare | live | pride | share | value |
| capture | deprive | glide | lodge | propose | shave | wade |
| care | desire | grade | lose | prove | shuffle | wage |
| celebrate | devise | graze | love | puzzle | sizzle | wake |
| choose | devote | grope | make | quake | skate | waste |
| chuckle | dine | grudge | meddle | race | slave | wave |
| close | dilute | grumble | mime | raise | slide | wheeze |
| combine | dive | guide | mine | rake | smile | whine |
| come | divide | gurgle | move | rate | smoke | wipe |
| compare | dodge | guzzle | muffle | rattle | sneeze | wobble |
| compete | doze | hate | mumble | rave | snore | wrestle |
| complete | drape | hide | name | receive | spare | write |
| compose | dredge | hike | nestle | recite | stare | |
| conclude | dribble | hire | nibble | refine | stifle | |
| confuse | elope | hobble | note | refuse | store | |
| console | escape | hope | nudge | require | stride | |
| consume | examine | hose | operate | rescue | strike | |

# Appendix 3    Words ending in 'y'

The words below are all nouns and verbs ending in 'y'. They are arranged in two lists depending on whether there is a vowel before the final 'y' (*just add* the suffix), or whether 'y' is preceded by a consonant (*change 'y' to 'i'* when adding the suffix.)

## JUST ADD

| | | | | | |
|---|---|---|---|---|---|
| abbey | buy | employ | joy | pray | storey |
| alley | chimney | enjoy | key | prey | survey |
| annoy | convey | essay | kidney | pulley | sway |
| array | curtsey | galley | medley | purvey | tray |
| bay | day | guy | monkey | quay | toy |
| betray | deploy | jay | obey | ray | trolley |
| boy | destroy | jersey | osprey | say | turkey |
| bray | dismay | jockey | play | spray | valley |
| buoy | donkey | journey | portray | stay | way |

## CHANGE 'y' to 'i'

| | | | | | |
|---|---|---|---|---|---|
| ability | charity | dry | identify | pastry | solidify |
| academy | cherry | duty | impurity | penalty | speciality |
| activity | city | dynasty | intensify | penny | specify |
| agency | clarify | economy | jelly | personality | spy |
| allergy | classify | eddy | jetty | pity | story |
| ally | comedy | effigy | jury | policy | strategy |
| amenity | commodity | elegy | justify | possibility | study |
| amplify | community | embassy | lady | pregnancy | subsidy |
| anomaly | comply | emergency | legacy | pony | supply |
| anthology | conspiracy | enemy | levy | priority | technology |
| anxiety | copy | facility | lobby | probability | teddy |
| apply | country | fairy | locality | prophecy | tenancy |
| army | county | falsify | lorry | prophesy | tendency |
| assembly | courtesy | fancy | lullaby | purify | terrify |
| atrocity | currency | fantasy | magnify | quality | testify |
| authority | curry | fatality | malady | quantity | tidy |
| baby | curtsy | ferry | marry | query | tragedy |
| battery | dairy | festivity | melody | rally | transparency |
| beautify | daisy | flurry | modify | ratify | try |
| berry | deformity | fly | mortify | rectify | typify |
| body | defy | formality | multiply | redundancy | unify |
| bully | deity | fortify | mystery | rely | utility |
| bury | democracy | frisby | mystify | remedy | vacancy |
| butterfly | deny | gallery | nanny | reply | variety |
| caddy | deputy | glorify | nappy | ruby | verify |
| candy | dhingy | gratify | notify | scurry | vilify |
| calamity | diary | gully | novelty | shandy | wallaby |
| carry | difficulty | gypsy | opportunity | signify | worry |
| casualty | dignify | hobby | pansy | similarity | |
| cavity | disqualify | horrify | parody | simplify | |
| celebrity | dolly | hurry | party | sky | |

# Appendix 4     Suffix 'y'

Words with suffix 'y' are arranged in three groups according to which suffixing rule is needed to add 'y' to the base word. Most base words just add the suffix, but those with V̆C pattern require the *doubling* rule, while base words ending in 'e' require the *drop 'e'* rule.

| JUST ADD | frosty | oily | steely | groggy | lazy |
|---|---|---|---|---|---|
| airy | frothy | panic(k)y | sticky | grubby | lousy |
| beady | fruity | papery | stormy | grotty | mousy |
| beefy | fussy | patchy | stretchy | knotty | nervy |
| bloody | glassy | pearly | stringy | muddy | noisy |
| blotchy | gloomy | peppery | stuffy | nutty | nosy |
| bossy | glossy | plucky | sulky | skinny | pricy |
| brainy | grainy | puffy | summery | sloppy | prickly |
| bulky | grassy | rainy | swampy | slummy | ropy |
| bumpy | greedy | risky | tangy | smoggy | rosy |
| bushy | guilty | rocky | thrifty | smutty | rumbly |
| catchy | hairy | roomy | thundery | spotty | shady |
| chilly | handy | rubbery | toothy | starry | shaky |
| classy | healthy | rusty | trendy | stubby | shiny |
| cloudy | hearty | salty | tricky | sunny | slimy |
| crafty | heathery | sandy | watery | tinny | smoky |
| creaky | hilly | scratchy | waxy | witty | snaky |
| creamy | huffy | scruffy | wealthy | | spicy |
| creepy | husky | seedy | weepy | DROP 'e' | spiky |
| crispy | inky | shivery | weighty | bony | spindly |
| crusty | itchy | showy | windy | bouncy | spongy |
| curly | jaunty | showery | wispy | breezy | stony |
| dewy | jerky | silky | wintery | bristly | stripy |
| dirty | jumpy | silvery | wordy | bubbly | stubbly |
| dreamy | leafy | sketchy | worthy | cheesy | tasty |
| dressy | leaky | skimpy | yellowy | choosy | tingly |
| dumpy | leathery | sleepy | | crazy | twinkly |
| dusky | lengthy | slushy | DOUBLE | crinkly | wavy |
| dusty | lucky | smelly | baggy | crumbly | wiry |
| earthy | lumpy | sneaky | batty | cuddly | wobbly |
| feathery | marshy | sniffy | bitty | dopy | wrinkly |
| filthy | meaty | snowy | chatty | dozy | |
| fishy | messy | soapy | choppy | drizzly | |
| fizzy | mighty | sooty | chummy | fiddly | |
| fleshy | milky | speedy | craggy | flaky | |
| flowery | minty | spidery | dotty | fleecy | |
| fluffy | moody | spooky | fatty | freckly | |
| foamy | mouldy | sporty | flabby | giggly | |
| foxy | mushy | squally | foggy | greasy | |
| freaky | musty | squeaky | funny | grimy | |
| frilly | murky | starchy | furry | icy | |
| frizzy | needy | steamy | gritty | juicy | |

# Appendix 5    Suffixes 'ful' and 'less'

The words below all end in 'ful' or 'less'. Those marked with an asterisk require the *change* rule when adding the suffix to the base word.

### Suffix 'ful'

| | | | | | |
|---|---|---|---|---|---|
| | colourful | forkful | *merciful | roomful | thankful |
| armful | deceitful | fretful | mindful | sackful | thoughtful |
| artful | delightful | frightful | (mis)trustful | scornful | (un)truthful |
| awful | (dis)dainful | fruitful | mournful | shameful | tuneful |
| bagful | (dis)trustful | glassful | mouthful | shovelful | useful |
| basketful | doubtful | gleeful | needful | sinful | wasteful |
| *beautiful | dreadful | (dis)graceful | neglectful | skilful | watchful |
| blissful | *dutiful | (un)grateful | plateful | sorrowful | wishful |
| boastful | (un)eventful | handful | playful | soulful | wistful |
| bottleful | (un)faithful | harmful | *plentiful | spadeful | woeful |
| bountiful | *fanciful | hateful | pocketful | spiteful | wonderful |
| boxful | fateful | (un)helpful | powerful | spoonful | wrongful |
| brimful | fearful | hopeful | purposeful | stressful | youthful |
| bucketful | fistful | hurtful | reproachful | (un)successful | zestful |
| cupful | fitful | joyful | respectful | tactful | |
| careful | forceful | (un)lawful | revengeful | tankful | |
| cheerful | forgetful | meaningful | rightful | (dis)tasteful | |

### Suffix 'less'

| | | | | | |
|---|---|---|---|---|---|
| | cloudless | friendless | loveless | remorseless | tactless |
| ageless | clueless | fruitless | luckless | restless | tasteless |
| aimless | colourless | godless | matchless | rootless | thankless |
| airless | comfortless | groundless | meaningless | ruthless | thoughtless |
| artless | cordless | hairless | *merciless | seedless | timeless |
| backless | countless | harmless | mindless | selfless | tireless |
| baseless | defenceless | hatless | moonless | senseless | toneless |
| beardless | doubtless | headless | motherless | shameless | toothless |
| blameless | dreamless | heartless | motionless | shapeless | topless |
| bloodless | driverless | heedless | motiveless | sightless | treeless |
| *bodiless | effortless | helpless | nameless | sinless | tuneless |
| boneless | endless | homeless | needless | sleepless | useless |
| bootless | eyeless | hopeless | noiseless | sleeveless | voiceless |
| bottomless | faceless | humourless | odourless | smokeless | weightless |
| boundless | faithless | jobless | painless | soulless | windless |
| brainless | fatherless | joyless | *penniless | soundless | wingless |
| breathless | fathomless | landless | *pitiless | speechless | wordless |
| careless | faultless | lawless | pointless | spineless | worthless |
| ceaseless | fearless | leaderless | powerless | spotless | |
| changeless | featureless | leafless | priceless | starless | |
| cheerless | flawless | legless | reckless | stateless | |
| childless | flightless | limitless | regardless | strapless | |
| classless | formless | listless | relentless | sunless | |

# Appendix 6    Suffix 'ness'

The words below are all nouns ending in suffix 'ness'. Those marked with an asterisk require the *change* rule when adding the suffix to the base word.

abruptness
absentmindedness
aimlessness
*airiness
alertness
aloofness
assertiveness
attractiveness
awareness
awkwardness
baldness
bitterness
blackness
blamelessness
blankness
bleakness
blessedness
blindness
*bloodthirstiness
*bossiness
boyishness
briefness
brightness
*bulkiness
calmness
carelessness
cheapness
cheerfulness
cleanliness
clearness
cleverness
closeness
*clumsiness
coarseness
coldness
conciseness
consciousness
*cosiness
*craftiness
crispness
dampness
darkness
deafness
decisiveness
dimness

*dizziness
drabness
*dreariness
*drowsiness
drunkenness
dryness
dullness
eagerness
effectiveness
*emptiness
fairness
faithfulness
fatness
fierceness
fitness
flatness
fondness
*foolhardiness
foolishness
forgetfulness
forgiveness
frankness
freshness
*friendliness
fullness
gentleness
giftedness
gladness
goodness
greatness
greenness
greyness
grimness
gruffness
(right/left) handedness
*happiness
hardness
harshness
*heaviness
helplessness
helpfulness
holiness
homelessness
homesickness
hopelessness

idleness
illness
indebtedness
joblessness
keenness
kindness
lateness
lawlessness
laxness
*laziness
lightness
likeness
listlessness
*liveliness
*loneliness
loudness
lushness
madness
meanness
meakness
*mistiness
nakedness
narrowness
narrowmindedness
*nastiness
*naughtiness
neatness
nervousness
newness
niceness
*nosiness
numbness
permissiveness
playfulness
politeness
possessiveness
*prettiness
protectiveness
quickness
*readiness
recklessness
redness
roughness
rudeness
ruthlessness

sadness
*saintliness
sameness
selfishness
*shabbiness
sharpness
shortsightedness
shyness
sickness
*silliness
sinfulness
*sleepiness
slowness
snobbishness
softness
spitefulness
steepness
stiffness
strangeness
stubbornness
suddenness
*surliness
sweetness
swiftness
tenderness
thickness
thinness
thoroughness
thoughtfulness
tiredness
togetherness
toughness
*ugliness
usefulness
vastness
vividness
warmness
weakness
*weariness
weightlessness
whiteness
wickedness
willingness

# Appendix 7　　Suffixes 'en' and 'ish'

The word lists for suffixes 'en' and 'ish' are arranged in groups according to what rule is needed to add the suffix to the base words. There is a separate list for 'ish' words denoting nationality. The word list for the 'en' suffix includes only those in which the suffix changes an adjective into a verb (Worksheets 46 and 47). It does not include words like 'swollen' where the suffix denotes the past participle of an irregular verb.

## 'en' suffix

| **JUST ADD** | frighten | sharpen | thicken | **DROP 'e'** |
|---|---|---|---|---|
| blacken | harden | shorten | tighten | coarsen |
| brighten | hearten | sicken | toughen | hasten |
| broaden | heighten | slacken | weaken | loosen |
| cheapen | lengthen | smarten | | ripen |
| dampen | lessen | soften | **DOUBLE** | awaken |
| darken | lighten | stiffen | fatten | whiten |
| deaden | moisten | straighten | flatten | widen |
| deafen | quicken | strengthen | gladden | worsen |
| deepen | quieten | sweeten | madden | |
| freshen | roughen | tauten | redden | |

## 'ish' suffix

| **JUST ADD** | girlish | smallish | mannish | roguish |
|---|---|---|---|---|
| babyish | greenish | softish | priggish | slavish |
| blackish | greyish | stand-offish | reddish | stylish |
| bookish | hawkish | steepish | sluggish | ticklish |
| boorish | hellish | stoutish | snappish | whitish |
| boyish | impish | strongish | snobbish | |
| brownish | kittenish | sweetish | thuggish | **Nationalities** |
| childish | liverish | tallish | uppish | British |
| churlish | longish | thickish | wettish | Danish |
| coolish | loutish | warmish | | English |
| dampish | lumpish | waspish | **DROP 'e'** | Finnish |
| darkish | oafish | weakish | blondish | Flemish |
| devilish | outlandish | wimpish | bluish | Irish |
| dwarfish | owlish | womanish | brutish | Jewish |
| fairish | peckish | yellowish | cliquish | Polish |
| feverish | pinkish | youngish | coquettish | Scottish |
| fiendish | puppyish | | knavish | Spanish |
| foolish | roundish | **DOUBLE** | peevish | Swedish |
| freakish | selfish | clannish | prudish | Turkish |
| frumpish | sheepish | fattish | purplish | Yiddish |
| ghoulish | shrewish | foppish | rakish | |

# Appendix 8 Adjective List: Suffixes 'er', 'est' and 'ly'

The words below are common adjectives which can take 'er' and 'est' suffix. Many can also take the suffix 'ly' to make them adverbs. They are arranged in 4 groups depending on what suffixing rule is necessary to join the suffix to the base word. (Do not *double* or *drop 'e'* when adding 'ly' to base words.)

| JUST ADD | | | | |
|---|---|---|---|---|
| black | pink | fat | stale | jolly |
| blunt | plain | flat | strange | juicy |
| bold | plump | fit | sure | lazy |
| bright | poor | glad | tame | lovely |
| broad | proud | grim | white | lumpy |
| brown | quaint | hot | wise | messy |
| calm | quick | mad | | mighty |
| cheap | quiet | red | **CHANGE 'y' to 'i'** | misty |
| clean | rich | sad | angry | nasty |
| clever | rough | slim | bossy | naughty |
| cold | swallow | thin | busy | noisy |
| cool | sharp | wet | chatty | nosy |
| damp | short | | cheeky | pretty |
| dark | slight | **DROP 'e'** | clumsy | rainy |
| deep | slow | bare | cosy | rusty |
| fast | small | brave | crazy | salty |
| few | smart | complete | creepy | scruffy |
| fresh | smooth | cute | curly | shabby |
| full | soft | extreme | dirty | shady |
| green | soon | fierce | dizzy | shaky |
| hard | steep | fine | dozy | silly |
| high | strong | gentle | dreamy | skinny |
| king | sweet | grave | dry | smelly |
| light | swift | humble | dusty | smoky |
| long | tall | huge | early | sporty |
| loud | thick | large | easy | stormy |
| low | tight | late | empty | sulky |
| mean | warm | loose | friendly | tasty |
| mild | weak | nice | frosty | thirsty |
| narrow | wild | pale | funny | tidy |
| near | young | polite | fussy | ugly |
| neat | | pure | greasy | windy |
| new | **DOUBLE** | rare | greedy | witty |
| odd | big | ripe | guilty | |
| old | dim | rude | happy | |
| | drab | safe | healthy | |

# Appendix 9    Suffix 'er': (agent)

The words with 'er' denoting a person are grouped according to the suffixing rule necessary to add the suffix to the base word. The list is selective as there are many words with this suffix. There is a separate list for 'er' words denoting non-human agency as in machines and gadgets.

## JUST ADD

banker
bowler
boxer
bricklayer
builder
buyer
campaigner
camper
cleaner
climber
cricketer
defender
dreamer
drinker
designer
employer
entertainer
farmer
fighter
foreigner
gardener
golfer
hunter
jailer
keeper
killer
leader
learner
lender
listener
murderer
mourner
owner
painter
pensioner
photographer
plasterer
player
preacher
presenter
prisoner
raider
rancher
reporter
retailer
singer
speaker
sprinter
sweeper
teacher
thinker
trainer
warder
worker

## DOUBLE

baby-sitter
bragger
day-tripper
drummer
eavesdropper
fitter
globe-trotter
gunner
jogger
kidnapper
knitter
logger
mugger
outfitter
planner
potter
robber
runner
shopper
sinner
skipper
spinner
squatter

swimmer
tanner
train-spotter
trapper
winner
woodcutter
worshipper

## DROP 'e'

angler
baker
bouncer
carer
carver
commuter
composer
crusader
diner
diver
driver
examiner
fiddler
forger
gambler
hiker
joker
juggler
lecturer
lover
manager
miner
observer
piper
producer
rambler
rider
ruler
shaver
skater
smoker

smuggler
snorer
subscriber
toddler
trader
voter
weaver
wrestler
writer

## Machines & Gadgets

blender
bulldozer
chopper
cooker
digger
dishwasher
duster
freezer
grater
grinder
heater
lawnmower
lighter
mincer
mixer
photocopier
printer
sander
scanner
slicer
sprinkler
steamer
timer
tin-opener
toaster
trimmer

# Appendix 10    Suffixing Game

The main suffixing rules can be practised in the form of a matching pairs game as described below.

## Materials

40 cards (approx. 7.5 cm by 5 cm).
20 sticky labels, 5 red, 5 yellow, 5 blue, 5 green.

## Preparation

Make a list of 5 base words which *just add* the suffix, 5 which *double,* 5 which *drop 'e'* and 5 which *change 'y' to 'i'.* The 20 words selected in Worksheets 74, 75 and 76 can be used for this purpose, or the various Appendices used to create the necessary word lists. Try and use a variety of suffixes, including both vowel and consonant suffixes.

On the 20 plain cards which do not have a sticky label, write the base word + suffix as a word-sum, e.g. snap + y, dismay + ed, etc. On the cards with sticky labels, choose one colour for each rule, and write 'JUST ADD', 'DOUBLE', 'DROP 'e', or 'CHANGE' on the coloured labels. On the reverse side, write the result of adding the suffix to the base word, e.g., 'snappy' (on reverse of card labelled 'DOUBLE'), 'dismayed' (on reverse of card labelled 'JUST ADD', etc.). A complete set of cards should thus contain: 20 cards with no label with word-sums on the reverse of the card, 20 cards with coloured stickers, 5 of each colour, labelled 'JUST ADD', 'DOUBLE', 'DROP 'e', or 'CHANGE'. On the reverse of these cards are complete words which match the word-sums on the plain cards.

## Rules

The game is played like pelmanism and the object is to get as many matching pairs as possible. It can be played by two people, but is more fun if three or more play. Shuffle the cards face down on the table. Players turn over a blank card and read the word-sum, e.g., crazy + ly. They then work out the rule, and turn over the appropriately labelled colour card, hoping to find the matching pair. If they are successful, they keep the pair and have another go. If unsuccessful, the cards are turned over, and the next player has a go. The winner is the player with the most matching pairs. (As a sting in the tail, pupils can then be asked to spell their words from memory in order to keep the pairs they have won!)

Variations of this game are possible. For example, sets can be made using only 30 cards to practise the *just add, double* and *drop 'e'* rule, but omitting the more difficult *change* rule. Fewer cards can be used to make the game slightly shorter, as it can be rather time-consuming to play with a pack of 40 cards. However, pupils generally enjoy this game very much, become quite competitive, and are forced to use the right suffixing rule to gain a matching pair. As they also have to remember where the cards are placed, the game also exercises visual memory skills.

# ANSWERS TO WORD-SQUARES

**Worksheet 8**

| d | r | e | f | l | e | x | v |
|---|---|---|---|---|---|---|---|
| o | s | i | x | m | f | a | x |
| r | f | k | b | o | x | w | e |
| e | o | r | m | y | f | i | x |
| l | x | a | i | d | j | c | p |
| a | l | h | x | t | a | x | s |
| x | b | s | u | f | f | i | x |

box       reflex

fax       relax

fix       six

fox       suffix

mix       tax

**Worksheet 9**

| d | n | j | t | e | a | c | h |
|---|---|---|---|---|---|---|---|
| l | b | e | n | c | h | o | f |
| c | h | u | r | c | h | a | r |
| r | e | s | b | u | n | c | h |
| u | l | p | e | a | c | h | k |
| t | l | u | n | c | h | q | x |
| c | g | v | c | a | t | c | h |
| h | t | o | t | y | m | u | w |

bench       crutch

bunch       lunch

catch       peach

church       teach

coach

**Worksheet 13**

| b | a | t | t | e | r | y | o |
|---|---|---|---|---|---|---|---|
| g | e | j | o | c | k | e | y |
| d | a | e | h | o | b | b | y |
| o | r | r | p | e | n | n | y |
| n | m | s | o | i | l | c | k |
| k | y | e | n | t | r | a | y |
| e | r | y | y | o | n | s | v |
| y | m | b | q | y | f | d | h |

army       jockey

battery       penny

donkey       pony

hobby       toy

jersey       tray

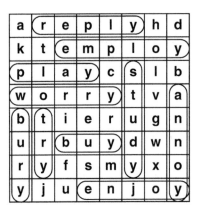

| a | r | e | p | l | y | h | d |
|---|---|---|---|---|---|---|---|
| k | t | e | m | p | l | o | y |
| p | l | a | y | c | s | l | b |
| w | o | r | r | y | t | v | a |
| b | t | i | e | r | u | g | n |
| u | r | b | u | y | d | w | n |
| r | y | f | s | m | y | x | o |
| y | j | u | e | n | j | o | y |

annoy       play

bury       reply

buy       study

employ       try

enjoy       worry

## Worksheet 28

| | | | | | | | | |
|---|---|---|---|---|---|---|---|---|
| s | t | a | c | k | l | o | c | k |
| b | i | s | t | r | i | c | k | b |
| j | c | p | r | i | c | k | s | l |
| m | k | i | c | k | f | v | f | o |
| l | i | c | k | o | c | w | b | c |
| p | a | c | k | s | h | o | c | k |
| i | e | u | d | p | e | c | k | l |
| c | x | q | u | a | c | k | y | g |
| k | s | m | a | c | k | n | h | q |

| | |
|---|---|
| block | prick |
| check | quack |
| kick | shock |
| lick | smack |
| lock | stack |
| pack | tick |
| peck | trick |
| pick | |

## Worksheet 33

| | | | | | |
|---|---|---|---|---|---|
| d | c | l | o | u | d | c |
| s | t | o | r | m | f | s |
| r | a | i | n | b | r | h |
| m | h | j | a | e | o | o |
| i | w | i | n | d | s | w |
| s | n | o | w | q | t | e |
| t | h | u | n | d | e | r |

| | |
|---|---|
| cloud | snow |
| frost | storm |
| mist | thunder |
| rain | wind |
| shower | |

## Worksheet 47

| | | | | | | | | |
|---|---|---|---|---|---|---|---|---|
| j | o | w | f | a | d | a | m | p | u |
| s | h | a | r | p | r | s | o | f | t |
| h | y | t | i | c | o | l | v | i | f |
| o | m | a | g | f | s | w | e | e | t |
| r | t | q | h | i | u | z | b | n | x |
| t | i | a | t | h | i | c | k | j | k |
| v | g | w | e | a | k | g | n | g | s |
| b | h | e | h | a | r | d | y | m | v |
| d | t | r | o | l | e | n | g | t | h |
| l | s | d | a | r | k | c | h | x | p |

| | |
|---|---|
| damp | short |
| dark | soft |
| fright | sweet |
| hard | thick |
| length | tight |
| sharp | weak |

## Worksheet 52

| | | | | | | | | |
|---|---|---|---|---|---|---|---|---|
| s | i | n | g | e | r | l | a | m | d |
| j | o | g | g | e | r | t | b | q | o |
| k | w | a | i | t | e | r | o | s | c |
| f | a | r | m | e | r | a | x | n | l |
| c | f | d | t | c | h | d | e | r | i |
| a | t | e | a | c | h | e | r | o | m |
| m | i | n | e | r | u | r | a | b | b |
| p | b | e | d | i | v | e | r | b | e |
| e | g | r | e | p | o | r | t | e | r |
| r | i | j | s | k | a | t | e | r | v |

| | |
|---|---|
| farmer | skater |
| climber | miner |
| teacher | gardener |
| jogger | diver |
| camper | waiter |
| singer | boxer |
| reporter | robber |
| trader | |

# ANSWERS TO RULE PRACTICE SHEETS

## Worksheet 71

| TEST ONE | | TEST TWO | |
|---|---|---|---|
| 1 | oily | 1 | heaped |
| 2 | witty | 2 | clipped |
| 3 | whiteness | 3 | bouncy |
| 4 | sneezing | 4 | snoring |
| 5 | madden | 5 | banned |
| 6 | guiding | 6 | slavish |
| 7 | nailed | 7 | moody |
| 8 | sluggish | 8 | spanning |
| 9 | peeling | 9 | spineless |
| 10 | poking | 10 | cloudy |
| 11 | cheesy | 11 | skinned |
| 12 | loaded | 12 | escaping |
| 13 | bragging | 13 | trailed |
| 14 | prickly | 14 | spotty |
| 15 | tinned | 15 | flaming |

## Worksheet 72

| TEST ONE | | TEST TWO | |
|---|---|---|---|
| 1 | deepest | 1 | rosy |
| 2 | smoky | 2 | brainy |
| 3 | redder | 3 | jutted |
| 4 | careful | 4 | dividing |
| 5 | slummy | 5 | tinny |
| 6 | proposing | 6 | widen |
| 7 | sagging | 7 | dopy |
| 8 | sipped | 8 | hopeful |
| 9 | timeless | 9 | whetting |
| 10 | glaring | 10 | slimmer |
| 11 | yellowish | 11 | cheapest |
| 12 | logging | 12 | freckly |
| 13 | ripest | 13 | steaming |
| 14 | sheepish | 14 | hooted |
| 15 | raver | 15 | fitting |

## Worksheet 73

player
witty
gazing
penniless
webbed
slimy
rosier
spiteful
cried
frying
prickly
silliness
slimming
staring
skidding
lazily
wasting
wasteful
lately
sinner

## Worksheet 74

lonelier
snappy
seedy
glider
nagged
steadily
crazy
floppy
prettier
shouting
sinful
dustiest
clapping
shiny
crazily
steepest
shaking
widen
padding
dismayed

## Worksheet 75

exciting
grabbed
bony
emptied
thirstiest
smoggy
blazing
employer
clumsier
hateful
grimy
splitting
steeper
simplified
peeled
wasteful
slammed
charities
arguing
grinned